WOMEN HEALERS
IN MEDIEVAL LIFE
AND LITERATURE

A WOMAN HEALER PREPARING A MEDICINE

Dorothy Hartley and Francis Kelly,
Medieval Costume and Life
(B. T. Botsford, Ltd., London, 1931), p. 130

WOMEN HEALERS IN MEDIEVAL LIFE AND LITERATURE

By MURIEL JOY HUGHES

Essay Index Reprint Series

BOOKS FOR LIBRARIES PRESS

FREEPORT, NEW YORK

LIBRARY OF CONGRESS CATALOG CARD NUMBER:

68-57322

PRINTED IN THE UNITED STATES OF AMERICA

To

My Father and Mother

ACKNOWLEDGMENTS

I HAVE GREAT PLEASURE in acknowledging a lasting debt of gratitude to Professor William Witherle Lawrence, whose illuminating presentation of medieval literature was a profound inspiration to me in the course of my graduate studies at Columbia University. I am especially grateful to Professor Roger Sherman Loomis, who has guided this study from an early stage to its completion. His counsel and scholarly criticism have been invaluable. At the same time, I am greatly indebted to him for whatever modern magic the study may possess. I wish also to express my appreciation to Professor Ernest Hunter Wright for his unfailing and kindly interest in my research work; to Professors Oscar James Campbell, Marjorie Nicolson, and Elliott Van Kirk Dobbie of the Department of English; to Professor Lynn Thorndike of the Department of History; to Professor John Lawrence Gerig of the Department of Romance Languages; and to Dr. Paul O. Kristeller of the Department of Philosophy for their valuable criticisms of the manuscript. For their interest in the subject from a medical standpoint, I am pleased to thank Dr. Elizabeth Mason-Hohl of Hollywood, California, who permitted me to read her paper on Trotula while it was still in manuscript, and Dr. Marion Laird of New York City, who criticized Trotula's medical procedure from the point of view of the modern obstetrician. Dr. Marion Osborn, Mrs. Anne Trinsey, and Sister Mary Catherine have been stimulating and gracious critics, and Miss Mabel Hannah and Mrs. Adele Mendelsohn have been thoughtful in ways too numerous to mention. For their continuous assistance over a period of years, I wish to thank the staff of the library of Columbia University, particularly Miss Constance Winchell and Miss Jean Macalister, and Miss Ruth Annan of the Rare Book Library of the New York Academy of Medicine. Not the least of my gratitude goes to Mrs. Mary Kout Dobbie and Miss Della Margaret Perrin for their generous aid in reading proof.

M.J.H.

University of Vermont
April 30, 1943

CONTENTS

"Ubi non est mulier, ingemiscit eger."
—Albertanus Brixiensis, *Liber de amore et dilectione dei*

"Wel may the sike man biwaille and wepe,
Ther as ther nys no wyf the hous to kepe."
—Chaucer, *The Merchant's Tale*

INTRODUCTION

Much of the responsibility for the administration of medical aid in the Middle Ages fell upon the women. At home they nursed their families through all kinds of illnesses; they rendered first aid for bruises and wounds, and attended to the needs of servants and guests. In the nunneries they performed the duties of infirmarian and gave special care to the sick. In the secular and conventual hospitals they were given what training was deemed necessary and then devoted the rest of their lives to nursing the sick.

These duties fell so obviously within women's sphere that they were naturally so accepted in much contemporary writing. Medical works referred to the practices of women healers from the professional point of view. Writers of medical textbooks recorded a woman's treatment of a special case either as a procedure to avoid, or as a matter of history and an example to follow. Historians, for the most part, were severe with the women healers and found in their practices more to blame than to praise. The laws of medieval cities and of university medical faculties also contained frequent references to women practitioners, usually in relation to their compliance with these laws. Custumals and visitation reports of the convents told of the faithful work of the infirmarians, sometimes presenting the infirmarian's complaint of overwork. Conduct books for religious and lay women alike occasionally set down their responsibilities as nurses, and sometimes even suggested pleasant household remedies.

References to healing by both men and women are found in the romances, *chansons de geste*, lais, and *romans d'aventure*. Although the themes were traditional and the atmosphere of most of these works was imaginary, the writers turned to medical practices of everyday life for realistic details and, upon occasion, even for dramatic incidents and major episodes. Laymen knew the general procedures that were followed in the care of wounds, sickness, and disease, and did not hesitate to write about them. Since the incident involving the healing usually constituted a minor episode in the story, the man or woman who brought about the cure ordinarily disappeared from the story after the patient recovered from his wound. In some romances, however, as in *Le Roman de Tristan*[1] by Thomas of Britain and in *Erec et Enide*[2] by Chrétien de Troyes, the major characters accomplished cures.

1. Thomas, *Le Roman de Tristan*, ed. Joseph Bédier, Société des anciens textes français (Paris, 1902), Vol. XLVI.
2. Kristian von Troyes, *Erec und Enide*, ed. Wendelin Foerster (Halle, 1909).

The subject of the woman healer in medieval times has attracted the attention of several writers. Dr. Sophia Jex-Blake was one of the first to become interested in it, and toward the end of the last century she wrote *Medical Women*,[3] a book in which she discussed the opportunities for women in the medical profession. In a brief review of medical women in all ages, Dr. Jex-Blake included only four medieval healers. She selected Abella of Salerno and Alessandra Gigliani of Bologna from medieval history, and the nun in the romance *Sir Ysumbras*[4] and Rebecca in *Ivanhoe* from fiction. In 1900 Dr. Mélanie Lipinska wrote an *Histoire des femmes médecins*,[5] a book which in 1930 she revised and called *Les Femmes et le progrès des sciences médicales*.[6] Dr. Lipinska cited many examples of women healers from both history and fiction, beginning with those of Egypt and Greece and continuing to her own day. In the section devoted to the medieval period she discussed Trotula and the Salernitan women, the group of French empirics practicing at the end of the thirteenth century, German and Italian practitioners, and many of the healers in literature. However, she made no attempt to classify them. In 1901 Haryett Fontanges published a similar study, *Les Femmes Docteurs en médecine dans tous les pays*,[7] in which she too referred to the French and Frankfort practitioners. In 1931 Dr. Kate Campbell Hurd-Mead published an article on the "Seven Important Periods in the Evolution of Women in Medicine,"[8] in which she devoted two of the periods to medieval women. In 1938 Dr. Hurd-Mead published the first volume of her comprehensive *History of Women in Medicine*,[9] in which she planned to present the subject from primitive times to the present day "with something approaching adequacy." Her first volume carried the study to the beginning of the nineteenth century. Dr. Hurd-Mead died before the second volume was completed.

Several studies of the subject of medieval healing have increased our knowledge of it and have indicated that there is still much to be learned about it. Dr. Eileen Power's essay, "Some Women Practitioners of Medicine in the Middle Ages,"[10] dealt particularly with the French

3. Sophia Jex-Blake, *Medical Women* (Edinburgh, 1872).
4. *Sir Ysumbras*, ed. Gustav Schleich (Berlin, 1901).
5. Mélanie Lipinska, *Histoire des femmes médecins* (Paris, 1900).
6. Mélanie Lipinska, *Les Femmes et le progrès des sciences médicales* (Paris, 1930).
7. Haryett Fontanges, *Les Femmes Docteurs en médecine dans tous les pays* (Paris, 1901).
8. Kate Campbell Hurd-Mead, "Seven Important Periods in the Evolution of Women in Medicine," *Bulletin of the Women's Medical College of Pennsylvania*, LXXXI, No. 3 (January, 1931), 6–15.
9. Kate Campbell Hurd-Mead, *A History of Women in Medicine* (Haddam, Conn., 1938).
10. Eileen Power, "Some Women Practitioners of Medicine in the Middle Ages," *Proceedings of the Royal Society of Medicine*, XV, Part 3 (1921–22), 20–23.

empirics arraigned in court in 1322. Her *Medieval English Nunneries*[11] was a thorough study of the various aspects of English conventual life. The history of nursing has been written by Adelaide M. Nutting and Lavinia L. Dock[12] and by Lavinia L. Dock and Isabel M. Stewart.[13] The history of hospitals has not yet been dealt with adequately or systematically. Rotha May Clay made a valuable contribution to it in her book, *Medieval Hospitals in England*.[14] Dr. Charles A. Mercier published two lectures on *Leper Houses and Medieval Hospitals*.[15] *Les Hôpitaux et la charité à Paris au XIIIᵉ siècle*[16] was the subject of a study by Dorothy Louise Mackay. Henry C. Burdett described a number of the best-known medieval hospitals in *Hospitals and Asylums of the World*.[17]

Information concerning medieval medical knowledge and special groups engaged in medical work may be found in numerous studies devoted to the subjects. Georg Manheimer's article, "Etwas über die Ärzte im alten Frankreich,"[18] presented a detailed survey of the procedures followed by men and women healers in Old French literature. Ida B. Jones showed the extent of general medical knowledge among English laymen in her study, "Popular Medical Knowledge in Fourteenth-Century English Literature."[19] G. L. Kriegk, in his *Deutsches Bürgerthum im Mittelalter*,[20] recorded the names of men and women practicing medicine in Frankfort in the late Middle Ages, and Ernest Wickersheimer furnished a valuable guide to French practitioners in his *Dictionnaire biographique des médecins en France au moyen âge*.[21] These studies have all contributed to the history of the woman healer in the Middle Ages. Other works will be mentioned in the course of this study. Of them all, only Dr. Hurd-Mead's *History of Women in Medicine* has treated the subject fully or has given an adequate picture of the woman healer against the background of academic medicine. Un-

11. Eileen Power, *Medieval English Nunneries* (Cambridge, 1922).
12. Adelaide M. Nutting and Lavinia L. Dock, *A History of Nursing* (New York, 1907–12).
13. Lavinia L. Dock and Isabel M. Stewart, *A Short History of Nursing* (New York, 1920).
14. Rotha May Clay, *The Medieval Hospitals of England* (London, 1909).
15. Charles A. Mercier, *Leper Houses and Medieval Hospitals* (London, 1915).
16. Dorothy Louise Mackay, *Les Hôpitaux et la charité à Paris au XIIIᵉ siècle* (Paris, 1923).
17. Henry C. Burdett, *Hospitals and Asylums of the World*, 4 vols. (London, 1893).
18. Georg Manheimer, "Etwas über die Ärzte im alten Frankreich," *Romanische Forschungen*, VI (May, 1890), 581–614.
19. Ida B. Jones, "Popular Medical Knowledge in Fourteenth-Century English Literature," *Bulletin of the Institute of the History of Medicine*, Part I, V, No. 5 (May, 1937), 405–51; Part II, V, No. 6 (June, 1937), 538–88.
20. G. L. Kriegk, *Deutsches Bürgerthum im Mittelalter* (Frankfort, 1868).
21. Ernest Wickersheimer, *Dictionnaire biographique des médecins en France au moyen âge* (Paris, 1936).

fortunately, her historical and literary references are not always accurate.

This study is concerned with the woman healer and her practices from the eleventh through the fifteenth century, with special emphasis upon the English woman. Though miraculous cures were attributed to female saints and offer an interesting subject for inquiry, they are not included here, since they belong rather to the realm of religious psychology and hagiology. Likewise, purely magical practices and their supposed influence on health, though fascinating enough to the imagination, are excluded for similar reasons. However, since the medieval mind drew no sharp line between the natural and the supernatural, the reader will not be surprised to find in the following pages fays or enchantresses who do not resort to magic but employ homely, or even scientific remedies, and to discover, on the other hand, that a prescription of herbs was supposed to acquire added potency from the recital of a charm. A certain amount of overlapping into the sphere of enchantment and witchcraft is unavoidable.

Our first chapter introduces us to some of the famous ladies of medieval literature who practiced the arts of healing or ventured to prescribe for ailments. Among these were Isolt and Nicolette, whose ministrations were so interesting that they suggested a fuller investigation of the actual medical practices of medieval women and the reflection of those practices in literature. We shall follow in succeeding chapters a systematic classification of the various kinds of healers: the practicing physicians and surgeons, the nurses, and the midwives. We shall draw on history and literature for light on their procedures and their social status. We shall show that, as one might expect, the records bear out, in the main, what imaginative literature describes. The herbals tell of the medicinal properties of the herbs which constitute the major part of the remedies employed by women in fiction. The writings of Hildegarde demonstrate the knowledge of herbs and medicine which an abbess might acquire, and they explain the reason why a nun occasionally plays the role of healer in the romances. And the gynecological treatise ascribed to Dame Trotula shows the importance of the midwife in medieval society and suggests the wide range of her activities outside her special work.

Chapter One

SOME FAMOUS WOMEN HEALERS IN LITERATURE

V IVID GLIMPSES of the medieval woman in the exercise of her therapeutic skills may be found in the belles lettres of the period. We see them, queen and slave girl, enchantress and housewife, meeting a great variety of situations, romantic and unromantic, and treating all manner of ailments, from nightmare to gangrene. We have hints as to their training, and gain some insight into their procedures.

Of these ladies of fiction some have attained world-wide renown, and their names are still familiar. Two of them were queens, both of whom won distinction for their medical skill. Queen Morgan le Fay, or Morgan the Wise, who had "learned what useful properties all the herbs contain"[1] in order to cure sick bodies, employed the usual medieval remedies, regardless of whether she wished to produce baleful or beneficial results. When, for example, in Malory's *Morte Darthur*[2] Sir Alexander received sixteen great wounds, Morgan le Fay "serched his wounds," and because she wished to prolong his cure, she gave him an ointment that all but caused his death. The following morning she relieved his pain with other ointments. Later, she drugged him with a potion that made him sleep for three days. After he promised to remain with her a twelvemonth and a day, she brought about a complete recovery. In *Erec et Enide*,[3] Morgan the Wise made for Erec a plaster which possessed the virtue of curing any wound, nerve, or joint on which it was laid once a day. Her greatest achievement as mistress of the healing art was her cure of Arthur's wounds in the Isle of Avalon, to which he was taken after the fatal battle with Mordred.[4]

1. *The Vita Merlini*, ed. John Jay Parry, "University of Illinois Studies in Language and Literature," X, No. 3 (1925), 326, 327.
2. Sir Thomas Malory, *Le Morte Darthur*, ed. H. Oskar Sommer (London, 1889), Bk. II, Chap. IX.
3. Kristian von Troyes, *Erec und Enide*, ed. Wendelin Foerster (Halle, 1909), ll. 4222–28.
4. By the time of *The Vita Merlini*, the middle of the twelfth century, Morgan seems to have been established as the healer in Avalon. See *The Vita Merlini*, ll. 916–18. The *Morte Arthure* of 1440 (ed. James Orchard Halliwell [Brixton Hall, 1847], p. 360) stated that a surgeon from Salerno was called in to "search" Arthur's wounds. For a discussion of Morgan as a healer of Arthur in Avalon, see Lucy Allen Paton, *Studies in the Fairy Mythology of Arthurian Romance* (Boston, 1903), pp. 25–28 and *passim*; *Review of English Studies*, X (1934), 81 f.

Queen Isolt of Ireland was perhaps the most renowned of all the women healers in fiction. She alone knew "the nature of all the herbs and their virtue and all manner of salves that may heal wounds."[5] We find a full account of her ministrations in the Old Norse *Tristrams Saga*, translated in 1226 from the famous Anglo-Norman poem of Thomas. In the traditional manner of all women, this queen passed her medical knowledge on to her daughter, Isolt, the heroine of the story, and final tragedy overtakes the lovers because circumstances did not permit the Princess to use her skill. The plot is unusual in that the principal action is closely linked to the healing of Tristram. Twice the Queen cured Tristram's wounds, and each time with momentous consequences for him and her daughter.

According to the romance, in the year when England was to pay her tribute of boys to Ireland, Tristram took it upon himself to free the country of this bondage and to kill Morhaut, the powerful champion sent each summer to collect the truage. After a fierce combat, Morhaut wounded Tristram in the left side, and warned him that, since the sword was poisoned on both edges, all wounds inflicted by it would be mortal. Furthermore, the only leech who could heal the wound was his sister, the Queen. Therefore, it would be far better for Tristram to yield, to be healed by the Queen, and to become Morhaut's friend. Insulted by such an offer, Tristram smote his opponent's helmet with such force that he sundered the steel and pierced the brainpan. He attempted to pull his sword free, but the point broke off and stuck in the wound, so that Morhaut fell from his horse, dead.

Morhaut's warning proved true. Tristram became an outcast from society because of his poisoned wound, which no doctor could cure, and the stench from which no one could bear. As a last resort, he sailed from England to the shores of Ireland, where he changed his name to Tantris. Because of his knowledge of harping and other arts, he was well received. News of his accomplishments reached the ears of Princess Isolt, who wished to have him as her teacher, but when he arrived at the Queen's chamber with his ill-smelling wound, no one could endure his presence. Out of sympathy for him Queen Isolt promised to heal him. Thus he became the patient of the one person in the world who could restore him to health.

The Queen went about the business of healing Tristram in the manner of a woman healer who was long accustomed to such practice. The saga

5. *The Romance of Tristram and Ysolt by Thomas of Britain*, translated from the Old French and Old Norse by Roger Sherman Loomis (New York, 1931), p. 72.

tells how she effected the cure. "Make ready anon my remedies of poisons," she ordered.

> And all that day she laid on him a plaster, and anon the stench came out of the wound, and the night next after the Queen took the wound with her own hand and washed it out with healing balms and bound it with marvelous plasters so that within short space she did away the swelling and the venom. In all the world leech was there none so knowing of all manner arts of healing, for she could how to help all manner diseases and wounds wherewith men may be visited. She was cunning in the virtues of all herbs that may be used unto any good, and wist all devices and means that pertain unto leechcraft. She knew thereto how to give succor against poisonous drink, and to heal poisonous wounds and perilous pains and all manner swellings, and to draw the smart out of all limbs, so that nowhere was to be found one more skilled nor of leechdoms a better master. When she had opened the wound and drawn forth all the stinking flesh and withdrawn the poison every dele, then all the living flesh seemed the better. Thereafter she bound on with her finger a plaster and healing ointment thereon so oft and skilfully that within a XL days he was as well healed as he had never caught wound: and hath become so strong and all perfect as he was erst.[6]

Tristram remained in Ireland long enough to teach the young Isolt how to play the harp, write letters, and make all kinds of things, until she became famous for her learning. He then received permission from the Queen to return home.

Despite the joyful reception of Tristram and of the tale of his deceit and cure, happiness was not long-lived at the court in Britain. Men became jealous and fearful lest Tristram with his skill and cunning should succeed his uncle as king and then wreak his vengeance upon those who had shunned him in his illness. They advised King Mark to marry, and counseled him to choose the lovely Princess of Ireland. Tristram, they suggested, was the only man who could win her. Fully aware of their guile, Tristram calmly accepted the mission and chose a score of valiant men to accompany him across the Irish Sea. They were to pretend that they were merchants until an opportunity should arise to visit the fair princess.

Tristram unexpectedly became a hero and savior of the Irish people. It seemed that a fearful dragon descended upon the town each day to slay all who came near him and that, in desperation, the king had prom-

6. *Ibid.*, p. 84.

ised his daughter to the knight who would kill the dragon. Tristram undertook the adventure himself, and made short work of the dragon. He cut off the end of its tongue as a souvenir, and hid it in his hose. Almost immediately the poison from the tongue affected his entire body, which swelled alarmingly. In addition, the poison bereft him of speech, so that he was in a pitiful plight.

Meanwhile, a cowardly seneschal, who had long loved Isolt, claimed the honor of having killed the dragon and demanded his reward. The Princess, knowing that cowardice did not turn to bravery overnight and suspecting some trickery, begged her mother to accompany her to the place of combat, where she might learn the truth. Not far from the body of the dragon, the two women found Tristram.

Once again the Queen had occasion to make use of her healing art. Tristram's blackened and swollen body was a clear indication to her practiced eye that he was poisoned. She prepared to revive him immediately. Taking from her bag a poison-herb, she put it between his teeth and administered it with some "treacle," a popular medicinal compound with which we shall deal in a later chapter. Tristram was straightway relieved of some of the poison. Servants bore him secretly to the castle, where the dragon's tongue was discovered. The Queen laid a large plaster upon his body to draw out the remaining poison, and she gave him strong healing potions to cure him internally.

When news of the seneschal's boasting reached Tristram, he agreed to defend the Princess in combat with the villain. At this point the ministrations of the women brought about a major crisis. In her solicitude for the health of Tristram, the Queen prepared many healing ointments and baths for him. One day while he was sitting in a medicinal bath, the Princess came to converse with him and to admire his knightly weapons. Drawing out his sword, she observed the breach which was made in it during his fight with Morhaut. She recollected that a piece of sword had been taken from Morhaut's head, and thereupon she secured the steel point from her coffer and found that it fitted Tristram's sword. At the discovery that Tristram was the man who had killed her uncle, she trembled with anger and rushed at Tristram to slay him. He pleaded with both the Princess and her mother, who appeared upon the scene, and reminded them of the coming contest with the seneschal. At this, the women relented and won the King's pardon for Tristram's deed.

Gottfried von Strassburg detracted somewhat from Isolt's fame, for in his *Tristan* he protested that Isolt's treatment of Tristram's wounds was not a fit story for noble ears,[7] and he therefore omitted the details

7. Gottfried von Strassburg, *Tristan*, ed. Friedrich Ranke (Berlin, 1930), ll. 7935 ff.

of it. They were also curtailed in the English *Sir Tristrem*, in which the healing is briefly described. The Queen, who "mest couþe of medicine," sent Tristram "a plaster kene."[8] The next day she visited him and attended to his injuries. She had a bath prepared for him, after which she gave him "soft salves" and drinks that soon restored him to health.[9]

Gottfried's modest scruples were not shared by the Bavarian knight, Wolfram von Eschenbach, who shortly before composed his masterpiece, *Parzival*, and gave the most detailed account of healing by women in medieval fiction. It was Arthur's mother, whom Wolfram called Queen Arnive, though more familiarly known to us under the name Ygerne, who superintended the treatment, and her patient was her grandson Gawain. Unrecognized, Gawain had entered the perilous castle where Arnive dwelt, had endured the rain of missiles from unseen hands, and had vanquished a fearsome lion, only to fall unconscious on the lion's body. The aged Queen, looking down from a window on the hero in this plight, sent two maidens to see whether he was still alive.

> One of them with her white hand removed his helm and bound his ventail back. She noticed a little fleck of foam on his mouth. . . . The maiden plucked a hair out of the sable fur [sewn on his surcoat] and held it before his nose. She observed whether the hair stirred in case the breath moved it. He was breathing. At once she had clear water brought in haste; her fair companion brought it with all speed. Softly the maiden thrust her finger between his teeth; then she poured water into his mouth, at first a little, gradually more, but she did not pour it too violently, until he opened his eyes.[10]

He implored the maidens to have his wounds tended by someone cunning in such matters or, if he must fight again, to bind on his helm once more. Reassuring him that there was no need for further combat, the maidens brought word to their mistress that there was hope of the gallant knight's recovery.

> The wise old queen had a bed set up near a good fire and had a rug spread before it. The queen also had precious salves brought in, which had been carefully prepared for concussions as well as for wounds. Then she ordered four of the maidens to go to him [Gawain] and take off his armor. They were to undress him carefully and to see to it that he would not be embarrassed.

8. *Sir Tristrem*, ed. Eugen Kölbing (Heilbronn, 1878), ll. 1204, 1208.
9. *Ibid.*
10. Wolfram von Eschenbach, *Parzival*, translated into modern German by Wilhelm Stapel (Hamburg, 1937), p. 332 f.

"Hold a silken cover about you and him and take off his armor underneath it. Let him walk, if he is still able. Otherwise, carry him there where I shall stand by the bed. I shall wait where the hero is to lie. . . ."

So then this was done. Sir Gawain was disarmed and led away, and aid was given him by those who could help. It developed that he had fifty or more wounds, but that the arrows had not penetrated too deeply through the rings, for he had held the shield against him. Then the old queen took dittany and warm wine and a piece of blue taffeta. With this she wiped the blood drops out of the wounds wherever they were, and she bandaged him so that he could recover. At those places where the helmet had been dented, the head was swollen. By this, one realized the force of the blows, but she healed the bruises through the power of the salves and through her skill.

She said, "I will bring you relief soon. Kundry, the Sorceress, is so kind as to visit me often. What can be done by medicine she has enabled me to do. When Anfortas sank into pain and suffering so that one had to secure aid, this salve helped him at least in so far that he did not die. It has come from Mundsalwäsche."

The Queen then placed in his mouth a root which caused him to fall asleep immediately. She covered him well.

Thus he slept the remainder of the day. Rich in honors, poor in dishonor, he lay, and he was warm. At times, however, a shiver ran through him in his sleep so that he started to sneeze and to swallow. That was the effect of the salve.

Many women passed in and out. They shone bright and beautiful. The old Arnive ordered with all her power, however, that none should gossip loudly as long as the hero slept. She also had the palace locked. . . .

Thus the hero slept until evening, when the Queen took the root out of his mouth. He awakened. Now he was thirsty. Then the skilled woman had a drink and good food brought to him, and he sat up and ate his food with great pleasure.

Many ladies surrounded him. Never before had he been served in more friendly manner than here. They nursed him with perfected courtesy.

And Gawain was a model patient. "With his olde courteisye," he protested against these noble ladies' standing about the sick-chamber, and addressed the Queen.

"My lady, this goes counter to my feelings, and ye might well hold me proud if these damsels here should stand in my presence. I pray you, sit, or partake of food with me."

"There will be no sitting here! Not one will take a seat but me. My lord, they would be shamed if they did not eagerly serve you, for ye are the fulfillment of our joy! . . ."[11]

With such competent and charming nurses, Gawain quickly recovered, and after a refreshing night's sleep was ready for his next adventure.

Marie de France reflected historic realities as well as literary tradition when she introduced into her lai "Les Dous Amanz"[12] a woman trained in medicine at Salerno. In the lai, a king in Normandy prized his beautiful daughter so highly that he did not wish her to marry. His subjects criticized him for his affection until at last he declared that he would permit her to marry the suitor who would bear her in his arms to the pinnacle of an extremely high mountain.

The daughter and a young squire grew sorrowful at this announcement, for they had long loved each other secretly, and the youth knew that he would lose the maiden unless he performed the seemingly impossible feat. The maiden then proposed that her lover hasten to Salerno, where she had a rich aunt who had studied the art of medicine for more than thirty years, and who knew a great deal about herbs and roots. The woman would doubtless prepare an electuary, with the aid of which he could bear her triumphantly up the mountain.

In accordance with the niece's expectations, the aunt prepared a philter for the youth which would refresh him in heart, blood, and bones as soon as it was drunk. The youth hurried home with the potion and secured from the king the promise of his daughter's hand. On the appointed day, in the sight of a large gathering, he lifted the maiden in his arms and began the arduous climb. So overjoyed was he at his burden that he refused to drink from the flask, but determined to reach the summit with his own strength. He paid no attention to the maiden's repeated pleas to drink the potion, and struggled to the top of the mountain, where he suddenly fell dead. When the maiden realized her plight, she flung the philter to the ground, and taking her lover in her arms, she perished of grief. Medicinal herbs sprang up wherever the potion touched the earth.

Among the women in literature who effected complicated cures was the charming Nicolette, the Saracen slave who was beloved by Aucassin,

11. *Ibid.*, p. 336.
12. Marie de France, "Les Dous Amanz," in *Die Lais der Marie de France*, ed. Karl Warnke (3rd. ed.; Halle, 1925).

the son of Count Garin of Beaucaire. The parents of Aucassin, disapproving of his love, placed their son in a prison of marble. There in his cell Aucassin mourned aloud the loss of his sweet friend, and recalled in soliloquy the marvelous but not unnatural healing of a pilgrim by a sight of Nicolette's slender leg:

> "L'autrier vi un pelerin,
> nes estoit de Limosin,
> malades de l'esvertin,
> si gisoit ens en un lit,
> mout par estoit entrepris,
> de grant mal amaladis;
> tu passas devant son lit,
> si soulevas ton train
> et ton peliçon ermin,
> la cemisse de blanc lin,
> tant que ta ganbete vit:
> garis fu li pelerins
> et tos sains, ainc ne fu si;
> si se leva de son lit,
> si rala en son pais
> sains et saus et tos garis."[13]

Nicolette also was confined in a chamber, but she soon escaped and fled to a forest, where she built a lodge. Aucassin searched for her unavailingly, until at last he was directed to her bower. When he finally dismounted from his horse in front of her hiding place, his mind was so full of thoughts of her that he fell and dislocated his shoulder.

13. *Aucassin et Nicolette*, ed. Mario Roques (2d. ed.; Paris, 1936), Sec. XI, ll. 16 ff.
> One day I saw a pilgrim,
> Who was born in Limousin;
> In a fit of madness
> He lay on a bed;
> He was sorely discomfited,
> Ill with a great malady;
> You passed before his bed;
> Then you raised your train
> And your ermine pelisse,
> The chemise of white linen,
> So that he saw your slender leg.
> The pilgrim was healed
> And quite sound, as he had not been before.
> Then he rose from his bed;
> He returned to his country
> Well and safe and completely cured.

Il mist le pié fors de l'estrier por descendre, et li cevaus fu grans et haus; il pensa tant a Nicolete se tresdouce amie qu'il caï si durement sor une piere que l'espaulle li vola hors du liu. Il se senti molt blecié, mais il s'efforça tant au mix qu'il peut et ataça son ceval a l'autre main a une espine, si se torna sor costé tant qu'il vint tos souvins en le loge. . .[14]

When he told Nicolette of the accident, she deftly manipulated the shoulder until it went back into place, and then she applied a poultice:

Ele le portasta et trova qu'il avoit l'espaulle hors du liu; ele le mania tant a ses blances mains et porsaca, si con Dix le vaut qui les amans ainme, qu'ele revint a liu; et puis si prist des flors et de l'erbe fresce et des fuelles verdes, si le loia sus au pan de sa cemisse; et il fu tox garis.[15]

Fantastic though Nicolette's treatment may sound, similar procedures may be found in medieval herbals and leech-books, and we can surmise that an occasional shoulder was actually set with the aid of a poultice made of herbs and flowers.

The *Prose Lancelot* was familiar to all courtly readers of the Middle Ages, and so we may correctly apply the adjective "famous" to a certain damsel whose name is given in one ms. as Amable[16] and who saved Lancelot from death by poison through her drastic treatment.[17] Very beautiful herself, she was smitten by the beauty of Lancelot as he joined a picnic party in a meadow one hot day. He quenched his thirst too liberally at a spring where two hideous snakes made their home, and fell unconscious. Amable's brother appealed to her to use her unequaled skill.

Lors vait par la proiere de son frere et coille herbes teles comme elle quide que bones li soient a venin oster. Puis revint arriere & lez trible au poing de lespee Lancelot en la coupe meisme ou il ot beu. et met

14. *Ibid.*, Sec. XXIV, ll. 82–87. "He withdrew his foot from the stirrup to descend, and the horse was large and tall. He thought so deeply of Nicolette, his very sweet friend, that he fell so heavily on a stone that his shoulder came out of place. He felt himself to be badly wounded, but he forced himself to do all he could and fastened his horse to a thorn with the other hand. Then he turned on his side so that he entered the lodge in a reversed position."
15. *Ibid.*, Sec. XXVI, ll. 10–14. "She handled it and found that he had a dislocated shoulder. She handled it and manipulated it with her white hands in such a manner that by the grace of God, Who loves all lovers, she put it back into place. Then she took flowers and fresh herbs and green leaves and bound them over [the injury] with the hem of her chemise. And he was wholly mended."
16. *Vulgate Version of the Arthurian Romances*, ed. H. Oskar Sommer (Washington, 1912), V, 424.
17. *Ibid.*, pp. 71–82.

avec triacle & puis li oevre la bouce et li en met ens un petit. Et il en but si comme il pot. Et il ert ja si enfles que sez gambes nestoient pas mains grosses que uns homme est parmi le pis et parmi le cors.[18]

Next Amable dispatched her brother to fetch all the robes he could find in her chamber and he returned with a horse's load. Lancelot meanwhile had been disarmed, and was now laid in a bed and all the covers piled on top of him. A tent was pitched to shield him from the sun. All that day and the next until noon he lay mute and motionless, dreaming of Guinevere and perspiring freely. When he complained of the killing heat, the damsel told him to suffer until the morrow. Then at prime she removed two quilts and three covers of gray fur, and discovered that the swelling had left him, but so also had his finger-nails, toenails, and hair. He was feeling much better and requested that his golden locks be placed in a box to send to the Queen! Amable then gave him a little food, transferred him to another bed, covered him lightly, and allowed him to sleep. When his cousin Lionel appeared on the scene, he was dispatched to Guinevere with an ivory casket containing the hero's hair.

During Lionel's absence of several days, poor Amable herself fell a victim to the malady of love and took to her bed, while her patient grew worse for lack of her ministrations. In this crisis Lionel's return was a godsend. He contrived to satisfy the damsel's modest yearnings by persuading Lancelot to promise, if he were cured, to be her knight all the days of his life. At once she rose from her bed, prepared food for the invalid, and after he had had a good night's rest, anointed his temples and arms with a wonderful electuary. A little more feeding and sleep restored his physical health. There remained the complicated emotional state of Lancelot, torn between loyalty to Guinevere and his promise to the damsel who had saved his life. Amable's resourcefulness was equal to this situation also.

Chaucer allotted the task of handling another difficult problem in pathology to Pertelote, the intelligent little hen in the "Nun's Priest's Tale," who advised Chauntecleer, her skeptical husband, when one morning he disclosed his anxiety over a dream of the previous night. In the dream he had seen a houndlike beast of reddish-yellow color, with black-tipped tail and ears, and glowing eyes. Pertelote made light of his

18. *Ibid.*, p. 72. "Then at the prayer of her brother she goes and culls such herbs as she knows would be good for removing the poison. Then she returns and bruises them with the hilt of Lancelot's sword in the same cup from which he has drunk, and adds 'treacle' and then opens his mouth and puts in a little of it. And he drank it as well as he could. And he was already so swollen that his legs were not less thick than a man is through the chest and through the body."

fears and, upon the basis of his nightmare, recommended a cure for his ailment. It was evident to her that Chauntecleer was suffering from an overabundance of choler and melancholy, two of the humors which were supposed to control the human system.[19] The superfluity of choler caused Chauntecleer to dream of such things as red beasts, while the excess of melancholy brought on dreams in which there were visions of black objects. Having diagnosed her husband's case to her satisfaction, Pertelote proceeded to prescribe a cure. Since there was no apothecary in the town, she would teach him which of the medicinal herbs in her garden would serve as remedies. With wifely concern she warned him that he must take care that the sun in its ascension should not find him "repleet of humours hoote,"[20] lest he contract a tertian fever or an ague. She then ordered the following diet of digestives and laxatives.

> "A day or two ye shul have digestyves
> Of wormes, er ye take youre laxatyves
> Of lawriol, centaure, and fumetere,
> Or elles of ellebor, that groweth there,
> Of katapuce, or of gaitrys beryis,
> Of herbe yve, growyng in oure yeerd, ther mery is;
> Pekke hem up right as they growe and ete hem yn."[21]

Chauntecleer promptly pronounced all laxatives "venymous."

> "I hem diffye, I love hem never a deel!"[22]

Miss Pauline Aiken has pointed out that Pertelote's medical lore is derived from the *Speculum majus* of Vincent de Beauvais, and comments as follows on her prescription:[23]

It is characteristic of Pertelote that the emetics she selects are of the *gravia* type, but her magnificent capacity for prescribing heroic treatment can be fully appreciated only in connection with Vincent's list of emetics, which runs, in part, as follows: "Ellebor album, *quod ceteris amplius trahit;* post hoc sunt catapucia, deinde grana titimelli & laureole." Not content with prescribing the strongest drug in the list, Pertelote adds the second in potency, and then, to make results triply

19. See *infra*, pp. 67-8.
20. Geoffrey Chaucer, "The Nun's Priest's Tale," in *The Complete Works of Geoffrey Chaucer*, ed. F. N. Robinson (Cambridge, Mass., 1933), l. 2957.
21. *Ibid.*, ll. 2961-67.
22. *Ibid.*, l. 3156.
23. Pauline Aiken, "Vincent de Beauvais and Dame Pertelote's Knowledge of Medicine," *Speculum*, X (1935), 281-87.

sure, one of the two which share third place in Vincent's catalogue! It is indeed fortunate for Chauntecleer that he is a skeptic in regard to *materia medica*.

But, harmful though her medicines might have proved to Chauntecleer had he taken them, she was correctly informed, as Professor Curry[24] and Miss Aiken[25] have shown, about the humors, the fevers, and the medicinal use of the herbs she mentioned, and she followed medical practice in her diagnosis of the dream and her suggestions for the cure. Little of the argument of the typical physician adorns her speech, however; she spoke in terms which were perfectly clear to the layman. Her speech implied that she presented only a fraction of her knowledge and that she spoke the truth when she said,

> "Of othere humours koude I telle also
> That werken many a man in sleep ful wo."[26]

A brief account of Chauntecleer's nightmarish dream was all that she needed for a complete understanding of the dangers he faced, and with these in mind, she delivered her opinion and advice in the forthright manner of a woman who was accustomed to settling the problems of her household easily and efficiently.

In these several famed ladies of medieval fiction we have a varied and representative group. Morgan le Fay, as befits one who had in origin been a Celtic divinity and was still in medieval texts referred to as a *dea*, *déesse*, *gotinne*, or *goddes*, was more of an enchantress than a physician,[27] and if she resorted to plasters and salves, it was only as a concession to the tastes of generations growing skeptical of sheer magic. Nicolette, it is not surprising to learn, could perform two sorts of cures. Like other medieval ladies, she had a way of lifting her long gown as she

24. Walter Clyde Curry, *Chaucer and the Medieval Sciences* (New York, 1926), Chap. IX. In his study of Pertelote's speech, Professor Curry has shown the extent of Pertelote's knowledge of the humors, the fevers, and herbal lore. She was supported in her remarks about melancholia by Avicenna and in those about choler by Avicenna, Galen, Rhazes, Arnold of Villanova, Haly, and Peter of Abano. Her choice of "digestives" was corroborated by that great authority on herbs, Dioscorides. Her pronouncement on the tertian fever was confirmed by Avicenna. All these sources will be recognized as those well known to Chaucer's doctor of physic.

25. Aiken, *loc. cit.* Miss Aiken proves that Chaucer may well have taken all the information Pertelote presents in her speech from Vincent de Beauvais's *Speculum naturale* and his *Speculum doctrinale*, as the two could have supplied Chaucer, not only with his scientific information concerning red choler, melancholy, and tertian fever, but also with his order of detail.

26. Chaucer, *loc. cit.*, ll. 2937–38.

27. Roger S. Loomis, *Celtic Myth and Arthurian Romance* (New York, 1927), pp. 192 ff.

walked, and one glimpse of her *ganbete* was enough to send a bedridden lunatic walking home, restored to sanity. Such psychological treatment was hardly adequate for Aucassin's dislocated shoulder, and here Nicolette displayed the pluck and the knowledge which enabled her to reduce the bone, bind and poultice the shoulder, with complete success. Queen Isolt of Ireland, Queen Arnive and her maidens evince a practical competence as nurses even by modern standards. From Marie de France we learn of a woman who had evidently received far more than ordinary training in the decoction of herbs, for her long residence in Salerno, the seat of a famous medical school, was evidently related to her knowledge. Amable, however instructed, was justly confident of her sweat cure. Finally, Pertelote is the clever wife who has read up on medicine in the encyclopedia. Whether by malice prepense or by mere accident we know not, she prescribed for her husband, who was suffering from nightmare, the most drastic purgatives and emetics in the pharmacopeia!

One may well be curious about these ladies of fiction. How closely do they resemble the ladies of fact? What reliable information do we have as to their procedures? What further light can we get on their medicaments? What of the relation of women to the school of Salerno and academic medicine? What of the famous gynecologist Trotula? Were there hospitals, where women served as nurses? What medical manuals and herbals were available to women who could not read the Latin text of Vincent de Beauvais? For those who may entertain a natural curiosity about such matters the following chapters will attempt to give an answer.

Chapter Two

THE LAYMAN'S MEDICINE

WRITERS of medieval fiction reflected in their works the contemporary interest in wounds incurred by those who took part in martial exploits. The period was one of tournaments and bloody battles, which involved the knighthood of Europe and called for physical strength and courage. People were equally interested in the treatment of other surgical or medical conditions. Broken bones, fever, leprosy—ailments which engrossed the attention of physicians and surgeons—were in turn discussed by laymen.

The layman's knowledge of medicine, which came from a variety of sources, consisted of a mixture of medical theory and usage, of superstitious belief and practice. From widely read books, such as the *Image du monde*, *Le Roman de Siderach*, the *Dialogue of Placidus and Timeo*, *Li Livres dou Tresor* of Brunetto Latini, and the *Liber de proprietatibus rerum* of Bartholomew the Englishman (Bartholomaeus Anglicus),[1] lay persons gathered a remarkable fund of information about the composition of the universe and of the human body. Chaucer, we have seen, equipped Pertelote with medical knowledge which he derived from Vincent de Beauvais's *Speculum majus*.[2] Furthermore, laymen increased their knowledge of medical treatment through experience as patients in clinics and hospitals. In so far as they were able to do so in actual life, they adopted the same procedures in healing the sick as were used by the university and hospital-trained doctors. But lay healers somewhat naturally failed to grasp the basic relationship of medical theory to contemporary medical practice, and consequently they were obliged to make use of whatever remedies they thought appropriate and to apply them arbitrarily. In addition, they inherited the burden of superstition that had descended upon the Middle Ages. They were inclined to attribute supernatural qualities to the remedies they used and to look for help to anything that seemed to afford a means of healing, even if such aid took them completely outside the realm of orthodox medicine.

1. See Charles Victor Langlois, *La Connaissance de la nature et du monde au moyen âge* (Paris, 1911).
2. See Pauline Aiken, "Vincent de Beauvais and Dame Pertelote's Knowledge of Medicine," *Speculum*, X (1935), 281–87.

The lay women healers who could profit by the medical information given in books belonged almost exclusively, as did the healers in fiction, to the ranks of the nobility and of the upper middle classes. This was due largely to the fact that the educational resources of the time were available principally to these two classes of women. They were, in fact, the only women who could read the popular medical treatises and compendia of knowledge, and they were also the only ones who gave accounts in their correspondence or in literature of their adventures in the realm of medicine. If educated women living in a cultural center had access to medical books, they could keep in touch with current medical practices. If they could read Latin, they could acquire first-hand knowledge of the remedies used by the masters of medicine.[3] If they were literate but could not read Latin, they could turn to the treatises in the vernacular which began to make their appearance in the thirteenth century.

The number of thirteenth-century French medical treatises in France and England suggests that women early recognized the value of these books. It was not until the fourteenth century that someone undertook an English translation of the *De passionibus mulierum*, an eleventh-century gynecological treatise, and declared that he did so in order that women might diagnose and treat their diseases. He stated that he had translated that book into English "because whomen of our tonge donne bettyr rede and undyrstande thys langage than eny other and every whoman lettyrde rede hit to other unlettyrd and help hem and conceyle hem in her maledyes wt. owtyn shewyng here dysese to man. . ."[4] Another English work on gynecology of the same century was composed so that "oon woman may helpe another in her sykeness."[5] In the fourteenth-century dialogues which Caxton adapted from French and Flemish to French and English, there is mention that "George the booke sellar" had in his collection "books of physike."[6] Evidently in Bruges, where the work was probably first composed, medical books were available to those who could afford them. Such was the case in England, too, when in 1469 (?) William Ebesham wrote to Sir John Paston, listing the

3. The women of the nobility, of course, had chaplains and other persons to read for them during the eleventh, twelfth, and thirteenth centuries. For discussions of the literacy of the lay women, see James Westfall Thompson, *The Literacy of the Laity in the Middle Ages* (Berkeley, Calif., 1939), Chaps. VI and VII; Eileen Power, *Medieval English Nunneries* (Cambridge, 1922), pp. 246–47, 276–77; and Herbert Grundmann, "Die Frauen und die Literatur im Mittelalter," *Archiv für Kulturgeschichte*, XXVI (1936), 129–61.
4. *The Legacy of the Middle Ages*, ed. C. G. Crump and E. F. Jacob (Oxford, 1926), p. 421.
5. *Ibid.*
6. William Caxton, *Dialogues in French and English*, ed. Henry Bradley, Early English Text Society, Vol. LXXIX (1900), 38–39.

books he had copied for Sir John and quoting the price of each. At the head of the list appeared the entry:

First, I did write to his maistership a litill booke of Pheesyk, for which I had paid by Sir Thomas Leevys in Westminster xx*d*.[7]

The "litill booke of Pheesyk" had doubtless been recommended either to Sir John or to his wife as one that contained helpful household remedies.

While some women were interested in reading medical books, most of them gained their knowledge of current medical lore from listening to, and no doubt taking part in, animated discussions of the subject. In all ages, people have been genuinely interested in the constitution of the human body and in the forces that produce good or ill health. In the Middle Ages, the classical theories of the four humors, the four elements, and the complexions, as well as speculation on the influence of the heavenly bodies on man's life, and the part played by charms and amulets in healing, absorbed attention. With Hippocrates (b. 460 B.C.), medieval men and women believed that men's bodies contained blood, phlegm, yellow bile, and black bile, and that these constituents regulated the individual's health and nature. From Aristotle (384–322 B.C.), they learned that all matter, including the human body, was influenced by the qualities of heat and cold, moistness and dryness. And from the facile writer Galen (b. 130 A.D.), they made the interesting discovery that men were also governed by "complexions." Recurring references to the humors and complexions in many of the literary works of the later Middle Ages show that these subjects were constantly discussed among the learned writers. Jean de Meun voiced current conviction when he wrote in *Le Roman de la Rose* that the elements all met within the body, as within a coffer, there to exist in peace.[8] And echoing the popular interest in them, Gower made the confessor in the *Confessio Amantis* explain the humors, the elements, and the complexions at great length to the young lover.[9]

Although an occasional skeptic, such as Petrarch,[10] registered his disbelief in astrology, the ordinary lay healer as well as the ordinary medieval physician did not doubt that the stars and other heavenly

7. *The Paston Letters*, ed. James Gairdner (London, 1900–1901), Letter No. 596.
8. Guillaume de Lorris and Jean de Meung, *Le Roman de la Rose*, ed. Ernest Langlois, Société des anciens textes français, Vol. LXXI (1914–24), ll. 17, 777 ff.
9. John Gower, "Confessio Amantis," *John Gower's English Works*, ed. G. C. Macaulay, EETS, Vol. LXXXII (1900–1901), Bk. VII, ll. 385–88, 401–37.
10. Francis Petrarch, "Epistolarum de rebus senilibus," *Francisci Petrarchae opera quae extant omnia* (Basle, 1581), Bk. III, i.

bodies exercised a profound influence upon man's nature and health.[11] Men and women alike believed that the stars were even able to determine the "complexion" of the body at birth. Planets, in particular, exerted some special influence upon the child before birth, and apparently they retained their power over his welfare and destiny throughout his life. In addition, the planets and the signs of the zodiac governed special parts of the body and all the illnesses that affected these parts. They could also ward off disease and accident.

The moon, no less than the stars, had an important part to play in regulating the human body. People had long been accustomed to the notion that the waxing and waning of the moon brought on a fluctuation of the humors, and that therefore medicine should be administered, operations performed, and blood let at specified times during the month or year according to the state of the moon. Thus the *Lacnunga*, a leech-book of the tenth century, had taught that blood must not be diminished on the last Monday in April, the first Monday in August, and the first Monday in January, and that these were also dangerous days for any medicinal drinks.[12] But to add to the bewilderment of medieval men and women, medical teachings on the subject were not all consistent, and the popular *Regimen sanitatis Salernitanum*, which was accepted as a valuable guide in the twelfth century, held that September, April, and May were the best months for bloodletting, since the moon then exerted its greatest influence.[13] The influence of the moon was also an important factor that had to be reckoned with in the planting and gathering of herbs, the chief remedy for almost all ills. For that reason, a conduct book, known as *Le Ménagier de Paris* (1392–94), which was written by a Parisian of the upper middle class to guide his young wife in solving household problems, described the most approved method of planting herbs during the waxing and waning of the moon.[14]

In spite of the fact that lay men and women possessed a considerable amount of theoretical information on the subject of medicine and healing, they knew infinitely more about the practical remedies to be applied to specific cases. The serious business of life was involved in learning what they could about actual remedies, from experience or from each

11. See Theodore Otto Wedel, *The Medieval Attitude toward Astrology* (New Haven, Conn., 1920).

12. "Lacnunga," in *Leechdoms, Wortcunning, and Starcraft of Early England*, ed. Rev. Oswald Cockayne, Rolls Series, Vol. XXXV³ (1864), 77.

13. *Regimen sanitatis Salernitanum*, ed. and tr. as *The Code of Health of the School of Salernum* by John Ordronaux (Philadelphia, 1870), p. 122.

14. *Le Ménagier de Paris, traité de morale et d'économie domestique composé vers 1393 par un bourgeois parisien* (Paris, 1846), III, 43–53.

other; but, even more, they sought to learn from and to emulate the physicians. The lay healers tried to imitate the doctors when, for instance, they prescribed antidotes for poison or when they took to heart the advice to pay attention to diet. No less an authority than the *Regimen sanitatis Salernitanum* advised them that:

> Ex magna corna stomacho fit maxima poena:
> Ut sis nocte levis, sit tibi coena brevis,[15]

and

> Si tibi deficiant medici, medici tibi fiant
> Haec tria, mens laeta, requies, moderata diaeta.[16]

The reminders of the physicians to eat and drink moderately, reinforced by the warning of the clergy to beware of gluttony, led to the general acceptance of the proverb that "Mesure is medicine."[17] Chaucer emphasized this thought when he pointed out that the poor widow in the "Nun's Priest's Tale" was free from gout and apoplexy because

> Attempre diete was al hir phisik,
> And exercise, and hertes suffisaunce.[18]

This desire on the part of the lay healers to profit from experience was to no small degree responsible for their success in healing.

Lay healers learned how to treat the everyday ailments that afflict humanity in the ordinary course of events. The methods they used were naturally determined by the medical supplies they had on hand or could get from the herbalist or apothecary. But they prided themselves, in particular, on their knowledge of the most efficacious ways in which they could use herbs; for these in baths, ointments, and medicines had long been considered the principal remedy for all diseases. Physicians used them in all sorts of mixtures, and consequently lay women healers felt that they were following the most enlightened medical tradition when they sought to build their reputations as authorities on the subject. They had herb gardens in which they took great pride, and from these they gathered the various herbs which they mixed with butter, grease,

15. *Regimen sanitatis Salernitanum*, pp. 50, 51.
> "Great suppers do the stomach much offend,
> Sup light if lightly you to sleep intend."
16. *Ibid.*, pp. 46, 47.
> "Use three physicians still; first Doctor Quiet,
> Next Doctor Merryman, and Doctor Dyet."
17. *The Vision of William concerning Piers the Plowman*, ed. Walter W. Skeat, EETS, Vol. XXXVIII (1867), B text, l. 35.
18. Geoffrey Chaucer, "The Nun's Priest's Tale," in *Works of*, ed. F. N. Robinson (Cambridge, Mass., 1933), ll. 2838–39.

or honey for the benefit of their patients. Their herbal remedies were given almost invariably in the form of potions, powders, confections, ointments, and plasters.

The fount of all herbal information in the later Middle Ages was Dioscorides' *De materia medica*,[19] in which the author described more than six hundred plants and gave their medicinal values. Other treatises which also commanded attention included Pliny's *Historia naturalis*[20] (*ca.* 79 A.D.); the spurious *Herbarium Apuleii*[21] of the fifth century, which originally mentioned 185 plants; and the *Macer floridus*,[22] which listed seventy-seven herbs and their healing powers. Since sections in most of the compendia of knowledge were devoted to medicinal herbs, the lay person who read them might recognize their place and function in the composition of the world. Thus, Isidore of Seville, in his *Etymologiarum sive originum libri xx*,[23] generally called the *Etymologiae* (622-23), enumerated almost a hundred plants, and Bartholomew, who wrote originally for preaching friars, described some forty herbs in the *Liber de proprietatibus rerum*,[24] first naming their physical features, then stating their medicinal properties.

Likewise the treatises that give information about the plants grown in medieval gardens enable us to get a fairly clear idea of the usual herbs that women had at their disposal and that would therefore compose the basis of most of their home remedies. Almost all these herbs can be correctly classified as medicinal, since medicinal qualities or special virtues in healing were ascribed to practically all of them at one time or another. Among these treatises in the early and late Middle Ages are Charlemagne's capitulary, "De Villis"[25] (*ca.* 800); Alexander Neckam's *De naturis rerum*[26] (*ca.* 1200); John de Garlande's "Dictionarius"[27] (between 1218 and 1229); Walter de Biblesworth's treatise for the Lady Dionysia

19. Dioscorides, *De materia medica*, ed. Curtius Sprengel (Leipzig, 1829-30).
20. Pliny, the Elder, *Historia naturalis*, ed. Carol Mayhoff (Leipzig, 1892-1901).
21. "The Herbarium of Apuleius," in *Leechdoms, Wortcunning, and Starcraft of Early England*, Vol. XXXV.¹
22. *Macer floridus: de viribus herbarum*, ed. Julius Sillig (Leipzig, 1832).
23. Isidore of Seville, *Etymologiarum sive originum libri xx*, ed. W. M. Lindsay (Oxford, 1911).
24. Bartholomaeus Anglicus, *Liber de proprietatibus rerum*, translated as *All the Proprytees of Thynges*, by John Trevisa (London, 1495 [?]), Bk. XVII.
25. Charlemagne, "De Villis," in *Capitularia regum francorum*, ed. Alfredus Boretius, Monumenta Germaniae historia (Hannover, 1883), Legum sectio II, Tomus I.
26. Alexander Neckam, *De naturis rerum*, ed. Thomas Wright, Rolls Series, Vol. XXXIV (1863), 274.
27. "The Dictionarius of John de Garlande," in *A Volume of Vocabularies*, ed. Thomas Wright (London, 1857), p.136.

de Monchesi[28] (13c.); Caxton's *Dialogues in French and English*[29] (15c.); and two other fifteenth-century treatises.[30]

Doubtless all the herbs mentioned in the fifteenth-century treatises were carefully nourished in the well-stocked gardens of royalty and other well-to-do persons, but even in the less pretentious ones would be found, we may conclude, betony, clary, coriander, dittany, fennel, hyssop, lily, mint, orache, parsley, pellitory, rose, rue, sage, tansy, and violets, all useful to the kitchen and to the medicine cabinet alike. In making their medicines, women could supplement these herbs from their gardens with drugs and exotic herbs and powders from the apothecary's shop.

Scarcely a disease existed for which these herbals and treatises did not supply a cure, and few herbs grew which were not believed to be beneficial in curing a number of ailments.[31] The practical aspects of this kind of knowledge appealed strongly to women, for they found in the herbs possibilities for the simplest and the most complicated mixtures, from which they could select the one they deemed most appropriate.

The medicinal properties attributed to betony amply illustrate the great variety of uses to which both housewives and physicians put the herbs, and the wondrous faith of the people in herbal healing. Betony was one of the most commonly known herbs, being familiar to herbalists in France, Germany, Italy, and England. Italians thought so highly of it that they created the proverb "Sell your coat and buy betony," and Spaniards expressed their appreciation of it in the remark "He has as many virtues as betony." The *Herbarium Apuleii* recommended it as being good for a man's soul as well as for his body.[32] It would shield him against monstrous nocturnal visitors and from frightful visions and dreams. Scraped and rubbed to dust and mixed with hot beer, it would heal a broken head very quickly. Among its virtues, Neckam listed, in the *De laudibus divinae sapientiae*, the fact that it would comfort the ears and the spleen, help the eyes, relax the stomach, and cure dropsy,

28. *Ibid.*, p. 161.
29. Caxton, *op. cit.*, p. 13, ll. 299 ff.
30. One was "A Fifteenth-Century Treatise on Gardening by 'Mayster John Gardener,'" ed. by the Hon. Alicia M. Tyssen Amherst, *Archaeologia*, LIV (1894), 157–72. The second was MS Sloane 1201 of the British Museum, ed. Thomas Wright in *Homes of Other Days* (New York, 1871), pp. 312 ff.
31. Thorndike, in telling the story of "Rufinus: a Forgotten Botanist of the Thirteenth Century" (*Isis*, XVIII [July, 1932], pp. 63–76), shows how at least one herbalist disproved the common notion that herbs were valued only for the marvelous properties attributed to them in the herbal treatises, and made his own experiments with herbs to discover their medicinal values. Some experiments of this type were doubtless carried on by the women in an attempt to find helpful medicines.
32. "The Herbarium of Apuleius," in *Leechdoms, Wortcunning, and Starcraft of Early England*, XXXV[1], 71.

the bite of a mad dog, and the ague.[33] Its popularity as one of the greatest panaceas among herbs is rather humorously if somewhat lengthily
illustrated in the description in an English rimed medical treatise of the
fourteenth century.

Betonye sethyn þese lechys bedene,
Þat kepyth mannys body clene;
Who so betonye on hym bere,
Fro wykked sperytes it wyll hym were.
In þe monyth of august on all wyse
It mwste be gaderyd, or sonne ryse;
Who so drynke betonye and hawe þe ston,
Be hys vryne it schall owt gon;
Betonye, boyled and dronkyn with hony,
Is good ageyn þe dropesy,
And a playster of betoyne
Is good to leyn to syth of eyne;
Jows of betonye with eurose [rose water] clere
Counfortyth þe herynge of þe ere;
Powdyr of betonye eke is good,
Medelyd with hony, for vyolent blod;
Ageyn þe host, with-owte lac,
It counfortyth þe brest with þe stak;
Þe lewys of betonye, with salt mad nesche,
Is good for woundys in þe heed fresche;
Betonye also, dronkyn and etyn,
Terys of eyne it wyll letyn;
Betonye sothyn, þe soth to sayn,
Is good for þe bolnynge of þe eyn
In lycure þat whych wyn men callyn,
Whanne þe eyne arn blod-fallyn.
Betonye, with rewe sothyn and dyth,
For-doth in-nurhed of mannys syth;
And betonye dronkyn sekyrly
Distroyeth venym in mannys body.
Betonye, sothyn in reed wyn clene,
Purgeth þe stomak and þe splene.
Iiij lewys of betonye fyn
And iij cupful of elde wyn
And greynes of pepir xx and vij,

33. Alexander Neckam, *De laudibus divinae sapientiae*, ed. Thomas Wright, Rolls Series,
Vol. XXXIV (1863), 472.

Alle to-geddere growndyn ewene
And mad a drynke þer-of clenlyke,
Þat purgyth þe neris mythylyke.
Betonye and plantayn to-geder þou take
And with hoot water to-gedere þou make,
As seyth Macer opylyke,
Þat coueryth þe cotidyan mythilyke.
Ʒif þou of vomites wylt hawe bote,
Make a powdyr of betonye-rote
And drynk it with water clene,
It distroith þe fe[uer] all be-dene.
Iiij lewis of betonye, dronken with hot wyn,
Purgyth þe rewme weel and fyn.
Þe seed of betonye in tyme
Is mythy drynke ageyn all venyme.
Powdyr of betonye with wyn, I wene,
Purgyth þe matrice and makyth al clene.
Who so take a bene-weyt[h]e
Off powdyr of betonye, with hony weel dyth,
And ete it after his sopere ryf,
It counfortyth þe stomak and mythys degestyf.
Who so wyll don a serpent tene,
Take a garlond of betonye grene
And make a cerkle hym rownd abowte,
And he schall neuer on lywe gon owte,
But with his tayle he schall hym schende
Or with his mowth hym-self to-rende.
Þorow all þis woorld here on grounde
Beter erbys may non be founde
Þanne betonye and mynte for þe stomak
And eke for peyne and werke in þe bak.
A playster of betonye, I þe seye,
Is good on þe thonwongys [temples] for to leye,
It abreggyth heed-werk
And ʒewyth brythenesse to syth derke;
And ʒif it be-falle to eld or ʒing
Newly to lesyn here heryng,
Jows of betonye in his ere do leyn,
And it bryngyth þe herynge ageyn.
Ʒif on hawe þe toth-ake,
Betoyn sothyn and wyn he take

And kepe it in hys mowth at ewyn and morwe,
And it schall drywyn away þe sorwe.
Who so for trauayle or for swynke
Vse erly or late for to drynke,
Vse betoyn fastande: in fay
He schall noȝt be dronkyn þat ilke day.
For alle sekenesse in euery stounde
Betonye is good, whyl it may be founde.
What maner hurt þat neddres hawe
And he mowe betony crawe,
He schall hym strikyn þer-on anon,
And all his wo schal fro hym gon.
Þat hawe I seyn with ye
In gaderynge of betonye.[34]

Betony appeared in early tenth-century recipes for medicaments and enjoyed even greater popularity in later centuries.

Especially commended by the layman as sure cures for a surprising variety of illnesses were the theriacs, the herbal compounds believed to be particularly effective as antidotes for poisoning. Galen had promoted the use of the theriacs, or "treacles," and had widely acclaimed their virtues after he had compounded one for the Emperor Marcus Aurelius, who took doses of it daily.[35] By the fourteenth and fifteenth centuries, different compounds were mixed for such widely varying ailments as leprosy, wounds, broken legs and arms, headaches, coughs, palsy, dropsy, eye troubles, the pestilence, and the stone.

In the popular medical treatises many of the theriacs were dignified with special names. "Godisgrace"[36] was the suggestive title given to a plaster which would heal all wounds old and new. Popilion[37] was an ointment, good for all kinds of sores, and *gratia dei*[38] was an ointment effective for both sores and wounds. The drink of Antioch,[39] known to

34. F. Holthausen, "Medicinische Gedichte aus einer Stockholmer Handschrift," *Anglia*, XVIII (1896), 308–10. Cf. George Stephens, "Extracts in Prose and Verse from an Old English Medical Manuscript . . .," *Archaeologia*, XXX (1844), 349 ff.; and Robert Max Garrett, "A Middle English Rimed Medical Treatise," *Anglia*, XXXIV (1911), 165–67.
35. Claudius Galen, "Ad Pisonem de theriaca liber," *Claudii Galen opera omnia*, ed. D. Carolus Gottlob Kühn, XIV (Leipzig, 1821–33), 216–17.
36. George Henslow, *Medical Works of the Fourteenth Century* (London, 1899), pp. 48–50.
37. *Ibid.*, pp. 52–53.
38. *Ibid.*, pp. 53–54.
39. *Ibid.*, pp. 77–78.

John Arderne,[40] was reported to be beneficial to the wounded and bruised. Drugs and herbs were mixed in the *unguentum album*,[41] an ointment which the Paston family cherished. It was good for "saucefleume," the affliction of the summoner in the "Prologue to the Canterbury Tales," and for scalding and burning. The making of sage, the decoction which Chaucer offered as a means of healing Arcite's wounds, and which was known in the fourteenth century as a drink that would "hele al maner wounde with-oute plaistere or ani outher selue,"[42] must have given any woman great satisfaction, if only because of the number of ingredients it contained. With herbs and greases assembled, she could make the drink as follows:

Put wort-lef þer-to and þe saue us mad in þys maner in may for all the ȝere most best gaderyd, anys, þe route of maþer [stinking may-weed], mous-here, dayseyȝe, þe crop of þe red netel, þe crop of þe red brere, þe crop of þe rede coul [cabbage], crousope [soapwort], and con-fery [comfrey], dayseyȝe, osmunde [royal fern], betayne, ribgras [ribwort], plantayne, riol [pennyroyal], scabiose, ground-yuy, ver-veyne, gratia dei [hedge hyssop], morsus deaboly [devil's bit scabious], violet, motfelon [knapweed], primerole [primrose], ius of cowslyppe, ius of treyfoil [red clover], euphras [ie] [eyebright], medwort [meadow-sweet], spigurnel, flowers of sausekele [chicory], endyue, hertis-tong, sorel, herwort [sow thistle], floures of wodebynde, astrologia rotunda [aristologia], alleluya [woodsorrel], melycote, trifoylee, croysay [cross-wort], carpus [fenugreek], chekemete [chickweed], rosmary, herbe water [herb Walter], herbe Ion [herb John], herbe Roberd, smalache [wild celery], camamille, tyme, persoly, borage, and wermod [absinth]. Take þese and stampe hym wel with clene woter in the porporcion of hem in þys maner; take as moche of anes as of all þe ouþer so þat hit be haluyndel and maþer be þe iii del of þat ouþer most del mousere and bugle, sanygle and pigle and brombugle; of þe ouþer eche on y-lyche moche, and whenne þes herbys ben y-stampid wel with boter lete hym stonde so clene þat ne best may come þer-to noȝt foure days or 5, take þenne boter þat was y-mad on may and set ouer þe fuyre and melt and scom hit wel and loke þou haue as moche of botur and herbes; put þenne þyn herbes in-to þy pot and let hit seþe so longe; take þenne an purfie [strain] þorw a clene cloþ and do hit in a clene vessel and let hit stonde tille hit be cold; take þenne and put in-to a

40. John Arderne, *Treatises of Fistula in Ano*, ed. Sir D'Arcy Power, EETS, Vol. CXXXIX (1910), 120.
41. Henslow, *op. cit.*, pp. 78–79. See *infra*, p. 47.
42. Henslow, *op. cit.*, p. 55.

pot aȝen and seþ hit wel and mult hit ofte and clense hit as þou dost
by-fore, and do þis iii tyme and do hit in a vessel of erþe; for hit ys þe
best drynke þat ys for a wondyd man.[43]

Baths were recommended as part of the regimen of health from a very
early date for their comforting and relaxing effects. Galen had approved
of them, and in his "De sanitate tuenda," he had advocated that those
who worked hard should take baths in very hot water, so hot that it
appeared to be boiling.[44] Mineral, vapor, and warm-water baths were
in great repute wherever they were found in the Middle Ages. Vapor and
warm-water baths were given at regular bathhouses where a moderate
price was charged for them, the sum depending upon the cost of the
wood and coal needed for the heating of the water. In Paris, in 1292, the
vapor bath (étuve) cost two deniers, and the warm-water bath (bain d'eau
tiède), four deniers.[45] There, criers of the baths called early in the morning and baths were taken then. Of the twenty-six proprietors of bathing
establishments in Paris in 1292, one was a woman; Aveline, l'estuveresse,
was engaged in the business and lived in the Rue Saint-Denys.[46] There
were at least four public baths in fourteenth-century Mainz, and in
Frankfort in 1387 there were fifteen bathhouses and twenty-nine proprietors.[47] In the fifteenth century, Würzburg had eight bathhouses;
Ulm had eleven; Nuremberg, thirteen; Augsburg, seventeen; and Vienna,
twenty-nine.[48] In Florence in the later Middle Ages as many as three
streets of baths were in use.[49] Rabelais, in Pantagruel, listed five well-
known mineral baths in France and eight in Italy, and added that there
were "milles aultres lieux."[50]

Belief in the curative powers of herbs led to their inclusion in the bath,
thereby transforming it from the ordinary to the medicinal bath. The
"Secretum secretorum" recommended that herbs appropriate to the

43. *Ibid.*, pp. 55–56.
44. Galen, "De sanitate tuenda," *Opera omnia*, VI, 184, 370 ff.
45. Étienne Boileau, *Les Métiers et corporations . . . de Paris . . .*, ed. René de Lespinasse
    and François Bonnardot (Paris, 1879), pp. 154–55.
46. Hercule Géraud, *Paris sous Philippe le Bel d'après des documents originaux contenant le
    rôle de la taille* (Paris, 1837), pp. 628–29.
47. Lynn Thorndike, "Sanitation, Baths, and Street-cleaning in the Middle Ages and
    Renaissance," *Speculum*, III (1928), 197.
48. *Ibid.*
49. *Ibid.*, p. 198. And see Robert Davidsohn, *Geschichte von Florenz* (Berlin, 1912), IV,
    337, 338.
50. François Rabelais, "La Vie de Gargantua et de Pantagruel," *Oeuvres*, ed. Esmangart
    and Éloi Johanneau (Paris, 1823), Bk. II, Chap. XXXIII.

season be used in the bath.[51] John Russell's *Boke of Nurture* suggested the ingenious device of hanging about the bath sheets full of flowers and sweet green herbs.[52] After the bath, the person was to be washed with a basin of hot fresh herbs and rinsed with warm rose water. The same book contained a recipe for "the makyng of a bathe medicinale," which was a panacea for any "grievance." It was prepared in the following manner:

> Holy hokke/& yardehok [mallow]/ peritory [pellitory]/ and the brown fenelle,
> walle wort [Danewort]/ herbe John/ Sentory/ rybbewort/ & camamelle,
> Hey hove [ground ivy] / heyriff [clivers] / herbe benet/ bresewort [bruisewort]/ & smallache,
> broke lempk [brooklime] / Scabiose / Bilgres [buglos?] wildflax/ is good for ache:
> wethy leves/ grene otes/ boyled in fere fulle soft,
> Cast þem hote in to a vesselle/ & sett your soverayn alloft,
> and suffire þat hete a while as hoot as he may a-bide;
> se þat place be couered well ouer / & close on euery side;
> and what dissese ye be vexed with, grevaunce ouþer peyn.
> Þis medicyne shalle make yow hoole surely, as men seyn.[53]

Leaders on the battlefield, both in life and in fiction, thought that many of the wounds received in battle could be healed in the baths. Therefore, they made arrangements for the wounded to be sent to the baths, which were probably the natural hot-spring and mineral baths. In fiction, the frequent references to the medicinal baths prepared by the women suggest that these also were universally accepted as a means of cure. We have already noted that Isolt used the bath, among other means, to restore Tristram to health. In *Beves of Hampton*, Josian made use of baths filled with herbs to heal Beves's wounds,[54] and in Malory's *Morte Darthur*, when Lancelot wished to escape from Elaine's watchful eye, he sent her to the forest to collect herbs for his bath.[55] Gower tells

51. "Secretum secretorum," *Tractatus brevis et utilis ad declarandum quedam obscure dicta Fratis Rogeri*, ed. Robert Steele with an English translation from the Arabic by A. S. Fulton (Oxford, 1920), pp. 96–98, 209–11.
52. John Russell, "Boke of Nurture," in *Early English Manners and Meals*, ed. Frederick J. Furnivall, EETS, Vol. XXXII (1868), 66–67.
53. *Ibid.*, pp. 67–69.
54. See *infra*, p. 56, for other references to healing by means of baths.
55. Sir Thomas Malory, *Le Morte Darthur*, ed. H. Oskar Sommer (London, 1889), Bk. XVIII Chap. XVII.

how Medea and her maiden prepared baths "with herbes tempered and assaied" for Jason.[56]

Herbal medicine reflected, not only the popular faith in it, but also the superstitions attached to all such modes of healing. The Biblical statement that God gave power to word, herb, and stone added a strong appeal to remedies including them. Consequently, whenever a cure was effected by any of these means, news of the miracle was spread far and wide and, indeed, often found its way into the medical treatises of the time.

Of all the forms of superstition, charms and incantations were the most popular. They were usually written, spoken, or chanted in the form of a prayer or invocation addressed to an herb or other agent, or to the disease itself. If they were written, the language was the vernacular, Latin, or some unintelligible, garbled combination of Greek and Latin. Written charms were carried or worn on a designated part of the body. The features which Grendon found in the Anglo-Saxon charms[57] as a rule characterized those of the later period:

(1) The conjuration was sometimes preceded by a narrative. (2) There might be an appeal to a superior spirit. (3) Potent names and letters were used. (4) Special methods of dealing with disease demons were developed. (5) The exorcist boasted of power. (6) Ceremonial directions to the patient and exorcist were given. (7) Incantations were sung on parts of the body or on other objects. (8) The time for the performance of the rite was stated. (9) There was an association of ideas between the charm and the cure. Whereas Anglo-Saxon charms were often long and elaborate, the later ones were shortened and frequently combined with other rites, which supplied detailed ceremonies.

Various features and types of the earlier charms were combined in those of the later period. Longinus, the soldier who pierced the side of Christ on the Cross, is named in an Anglo-Saxon charm for the stitch:

Longinus miles lancea ponxit dominum et restitit sanguis et recessit dolor.[58]

The Longinus story appeared again in a charm addressed to the "wyk-kyde worme" which the Middle Ages persistently believed bored its way into a tooth and caused toothache. Common indeed were the remedies, like the following one of 1430–40, that were directed at this "evil."

---

56. Gower, *op. cit.*, Bk. IV, p. 254.
57. Felix Grendon, "The Anglo-Saxon Charms," *Journal of American Folk-Lore*, XXII, No. 92 (April-June, 1909), 110–18.
58. *Leechdoms, Wortcunning, and Starcraft of Early England*, XXXV[1], 393.

A charme for the tethe-werke.
Say the charme thris, to it be sayd ix. tymes, and ay thris at a chare-mynge.

> I conjoure the, laythely beste, with that ilke spere,
> That Longyous in his hand gane bere,
> And also with ane hatte of thorne,
> That one my Lordis hede was borne,
> With alle the wordis mare and lesse,
> With the Office of the Messe,
> With my Lorde and his xii. postilles,
> With oure Lady and her x. maydenys,
> Saynt Margrete, the haly quene,
> Saynt Katerin, the haly virgyne,
> ix. tymes Goddis forbott, thou wikkyde worme,
> Thet ever thou make any restynge,
> Bot awaye mot thou wende,
> To the erde and the stane![59]

The numbers three and nine—magic to medieval ears and fraught with power as well as hidden meaning—were employed freely in casting spells or in directions for preparing popular remedies. Names of saints and religious objects were also deemed especially potent, and by the later Middle Ages they had almost supplanted words like "abracadabra." Charms, furthermore, took on the qualities of the herbal panaceas, and were thought to be powerful enough to expel a number of diseases. One interesting English example, dated by Skeat about 1400, would free men from worms, venom, gout, festers, and pain (rankyl):

This charme brouth aungyl gabriel to sanctus William, for to charme cristen men fro worm, fro venom, fro goute, fro festyr, or fro rankyl. Furst do sey a messe of þe holy gost; thanne sey þus,† In nomine patris et filii et spiritus sancti, as ueryly as ihu crist was god, is and schal be, and as uerily þat he dede was wel do, and as uerily as he took flesch and blood of þe uirgine mary, and as uerily as he sufferyd 5 woundys in his body to bye alle synnes, and as uerily as he sufferyd for to be don on þe holy croos, and on euerysyde was hanged a thef; and hys ryth syde smetyn with a spere, and hys handys and hys feet were perschyd with naylys, and hys hed crownyd with a crowne of thornys; and as uerily as hys holy body restyd in holy sepulcyr; and

59. *Reliquiae Antiquae*, ed. Thomas Wright and James Orchard Halliwell (London, 1845), I, 126.

uerily as he brast helle ȝatys, and his holy sowlcys þene he leed to
ioye; and as uerily as he roos þe thrydde day fro ded, to lyue and
sethyn stey up to heuen, and syttyth on hys Faderys ryȝth hond; and
as uerily as he on domysday schal come, and reyse euery man and
woman in flesch and blood, in þe age of thetty wyntyr; and as uerily
as þat is owre lord schal deme all at hys pleȝaunce; and as uerily as all
þis þat i haue seyd is trewe and leue it trewe, and is trewe and schal be
trewe. Ryth so as uerily þis man or þis woman, now be hool of þe gout
or of þe sciatyk, or of þe gout erraunt, or of þe gout ardaunt, or of þe
gout festred, or of al maneer of gout, or of worm or of cankyr. Ded is
þe gout; ded is þe sciatyk; ded is þe festyr; ded is þe worm; ded is þe
cankyr; ded it is, and ded it now be, if it be goddis plesyng of þis man
or of þis woman.

Neme þe sekys name; þanne say þou and þe seke also a pater noster
and aue. Say þis charm thryes on thre sundry dayis ouyr hym and
here þat sufferyth ony of þeise ma(la)dies; and ley þi ryth hond upon
þe seke place, qwyl þou seyst þis charm; and defende hym þat he use
noon oþer medicyne, and þat he forsake no maner of mete for hys
sekenesse. And for certeyn he schal be heyl with-inne ix dayes.[60]

Formulas for charm-making varied little from these patterns, which
demonstrate how characteristics of one charm were often repeated in
another.

Amulets of stones, gems, or herbs were thought to possess manifold
powers.[61] They could drive away diseases, avert infection, or protect
one from any supernatural or evil force which might be directed at the
individual. In story material the amulet proved a more convenient
device for healing than did the charm, for the hero or heroine had but to
wear or carry the object believed to possess healing powers and the
reader was assured that in due time the charmed one would be cured
or his life would be spared. Blaunchefleur, for example, in the romance
of *Floris and Blaunchefleur*, gave Floris a ring which was a charm against
water and fire, iron and steel.[62] Horn, in *Horn et Rimenhild*, was given a
ring which would protect him from all blows in battle.[63] A ring of similar
virtue is mentioned in *Sir Perceval of Galles*:

60. Henslow, *op. cit.*, pp. 144–45.
61. On the use of magical gems see Joan Evans, *Magical Jewels of the Middle Ages and the
    Renaissance Particularly in England* (Oxford, 1922), Chaps. IV and VI.
62. *Floris and Blancheflour*, ed. A. B. Taylor (Oxford, 1927), ll. 388–94.
63. *Horn et Rimenhild*, ed. J. R. Lumby, EETS, Vol. XIV (1866), ll. 563–74.

A mane that had it in were,
One his body for to bere,
There scholde no dyntys hym-dere,
Ne to the dethe brynge.[64]

The author of *Piers Plowman* described Lady Meed as being richly
clothed and wearing a crown and costly rings set with

. . . red rubyes . as red as any glede
And diamantz of derrest pris . and double maners safferes,
Orientales and ewages ¯. enuenymes to destroye.[65]

Nothing was dreaded more than poison, and since the sources of poisoning were numerous, an amulet which would prevent it was considered a
wise preventive measure.

Herbs were naturally employed as charms against sickness more
frequently than were stones, especially in fiction. A knight might wear
a charmed stone into battle, but he would expect to be healed of a wound
through the efficacy of an herb. Individual herbs were assigned special
healing powers. We learn from an English medical treatise of the late
fourteenth century that whoever saw marigold early in the morning
would be free from fever all day.[66] An earlier French treatise recommended that, for tertian fever, the sick man kneel before some plantain
at sunrise, say three paternosters, rub some of the herb between his
hands, and drink the juice.[67] Mugwort, if borne day and night, would
also prevent fever.[68] If a wounded person held two leaves of periwinkle
between his teeth, the blood flowing from his wound would be stanched.[69]

The rituals accompanying the use of the charmed herbs in the medical
treatises were usually ignored in the romances and *chansons de geste* in
order to expedite the cure of the patient. Thus in the *Eneas* dittany was
said to have such great virtue that as soon as one had swallowed either
the leaf or the root, the sickness would be forgotten.[70] Dragonwort, in
Parzival, was also endowed with the magical power of healing as soon
as it was applied to a wound.[71] Fauquette, in *Gaufrey*, used a charmed

---

64. *Sir Perceval of Galles*, ed. James Orchard Halliwell, Camden Society, Vol. XXX (1844),
   ll. 1858–64.
65. *Piers Plowman*, B text, ll. 12–14.
66. Garrett, *op. cit.*, pp. 154–55.
67. Paul Meyer, "Recettes médicales en français," *Bulletin de la société des anciens textes
   français* (1906), p. 43.
68. Garrett, *op. cit.*, p. 170.
69. *Ibid.*, p. 173.
70. *Eneas*, ed. J. Salverda de Grave (Paris, 1925–29), Vol. I, stanza 56.
71. Wolfram von Eschenbach, *Parzival und Titurel*, ed. Ernst Martin (Halle, 1900), II
   483, ll. 6 ff.

herb which, after it was infused in a potion, healed Robastre the moment he drank it.[72] Mandragora had the same marvelous effect upon Oliver's wounds, in *Fierabras*, for as soon as he had used it, his good health returned.[73]

But along with the superstition in the layman's medicine went considerable common sense. Chemists have demonstrated that some of the herbs which men and women used freely in so many different forms in the Middle Ages possess actual medicinal value and are retained in vegetable drugs and compounds today.[74] In fact, almost all the herbs which composed the typical medieval garden have been found to contain some property of value to modern medicine. Anise, fennel, and coriander, for example, are cromocorps, containing oil and having an aromatic odor.[75] The oil of coriander and fennel is a volatile oil. The powdered fruit, fluid extract, and the oil of coriander are used as flavoring to disguise the taste of active purgatives.[76] The medicinal action of clary is described as "antispasmodic, balsamic, carminative, tonic, aromatic, aperitive, astringent, and pectoral."[77] Hyssop is used with purgatives and in licorice powder.[78] The lily is used externally in cataplasms for tumors and inflammation.[79] Mandragora leaves are cooling and are used in ointments and other external applications.[80] Parsley has carminative, tonic, and aperient action, but it is valuable principally for its diuretic properties.[81] Several kinds of mint have medicinal value. Spearmint oil is a stimulant and antispasmodic.[82] Peppermint is the most extensively used of all the volatile oils and is used especially for flatulence and colic.[83] The root of pellitory is used to relieve toothache and promote the flow of saliva, and is therefore an addition to many dentifrices.[84] Roses are employed almost solely for their odor.[85] Rue is strongly stimulating and is used frequently as an emmenagogue.[86] Fresh sage is still applied in poultices for sprains and swellings.[87] Sage in infusions, as in a gargle, is used for sore or ulcerated throats and bleeding

72. *Gaufrey*, ed. F. Guessard and P. Chabaille, Anciens Poètes de France, Vol. III (1859), l. 3928.

73. *Fierabras*, ed. A. Kroeber and G. Servais, APF, Vol. IV (1860), l. 2210.

74. See John Uri Lloyd, *Origin and History of All the Pharmacopeial Vegetable Drugs, Chemicals, and Preparations* (Cincinnati, 1921); George B. Rigg, *The Pharmacist's Botany* (New York, 1924); and Mrs. M. Grieve and Mrs. C. F. Leyel, *A Modern Herbal* (New York, 1931).

75. Rigg, *op. cit.*, p. 124.

76. Grieve and Leyel, *op. cit.*, I, 222.

77. *Ibid.*, I, 204.
78. *Ibid.*, I, 426–27.
79. *Ibid.*, II, 483.
80. *Ibid.*, II, 511.
81. *Ibid.*, II, 611–14.
82. *Ibid.*, II, 533–36.
83. *Ibid.*, II, 542.
84. *Ibid.*, II, 622.
85. *Ibid.*, II, 683.
86. *Ibid.*, II, 696.
87. *Ibid.*, II, 700–707.

gums. It prevents the excessive flow of saliva.[88] Tansy is a tonic and anthelmintic.[89] And violets possess slightly laxative properties when used in sirup, which is also useful as a coloring agent in neutral medicines.[90] The properties noted here are by no means all of those attributed to these herbs, and yet they suggest the wisdom of the lay as well as of the professional healers of the Middle Ages in their reliance upon herbal remedies.

88. *Ibid.*   89. *Ibid.*, II, 779–80.   90. *Ibid.*, II, 838.

Chapter Three

LAY WOMEN HEALERS

In History

THE MEDICAL information which educated women of the Middle Ages gained and the uses to which they applied it are well illustrated in the literary works that were written by, or for, several of them. Not many women committed either their experiences in healing or their observations on the subject to paper, but those who did represent a widely scattered group of women belonging to different social levels. All were sufficiently well educated to read; indeed, two of them received as thorough a training in the arts and sciences as it was possible for women to acquire in the medieval period. One of the latter was the Princess Anna Comnena, who lived at the court of her father, Emperor Alexius I (1081–1118), in Constantinople. She was the author of *The Alexiad*, which was a chronicle of her father's reign. In her numerous allusions to sickness and health she showed that she had early received a thorough training in the quadrivium, that she had subsequently read extensively, and that she was able to apply her knowledge intelligently. The other was Christine de Pisan, daughter of Thomas de Pisan, astrologer and physician. Christine lived from about 1364 to 1429 and won renown for her ardent defense of women and their accomplishments. The letters of several women of the Paston family, landed gentry in fifteenth-century Norfolk, furnish a lively record, not only of the medical treatment the ladies were accustomed to give to members of their households, but also of the attitude which they adopted toward physicians. In addition to these, we have the book of instruction that a *bourgeois* citizen of Paris wrote for his very young wife, who could read but who lacked the education of the Pastons or of Christine de Pisan.

The medical knowledge of Princess Anna Comnena was almost professional, and at times it enabled her to grasp truths in advance of the doctrines and beliefs of her day. She suspected that there were other causes of illness than those accepted by the physicians:

It seems to me that if a body is sickly, the sickliness is often aggravated by external causes, but that occasionally, too, the causes of our illnesses spring up of themselves, although we are apt to blame the inequalities of the climate, indiscretion of diet, or perhaps too, the humours as the cause of our fevers.[1]

Her husband's tumor, she thought, was caused partly by the discomforts of military life, partly by the "varieties and severities of climate experienced," and partly by his anxiety for the family, "for worrying was innate in him and his troubles were incessant."[2] Her father's gout was not inherited, "nor was it due to soft living which often gives it to those who are intemperate in their life and pleasures."[3] Instead she attributed it, first, to an injury to the kneecap sustained while the Emperor was playing polo; second, to worry; third, to the talkativeness and thoughtlessness of the Franks who engrossed the Emperor's attention so much that he went for days without proper food and rest; and, finally, to the constant presence of some "intimate enemy."[4] One illness of the Emperor's she identified with quartan fever, and she reported that it caused his teeth to chatter with cold.[5] Duke Robert Guiscard, the leader of the Norman forces in Byzantium, was seized with a violent fever, she stated, but she did not know whether he died of the fever or of pleurisy.[6] His son, on the other hand, was forewarned of his father's death through a superstitious reference to Jerusalem.[7]

Anna mentioned numerous kinds of sickness, usually taking the contemporary, that is to say the Galenic, attitude toward them. She compared covetousness to gangrene, "which can never be arrested once it has attacked the body, until it has passed right through and vitiated it entirely."[8] She told of Charatices, a barbarian, who, after desecrating a church, "fell to the ground foaming at the mouth, and so he went out of the town mad."[9] His epilepsy she attributed to the "hand of God" and an avenging demon.[10] She called her mother's skillful ministrations "a good antidote" to the dangers of the banquet, and a salutary medicine for "harm in food,"[11] both of which terms recall Galen's use of the

---

1. Anna Comnena, *The Alexiad*, tr. Elizabeth A. S. Dawes (London, 1928), Bk. I, Sec. 10, p. 26.
2. *Ibid.*, Preface, Sec. 3, p. 3.
3. *Ibid.*, Bk. XIV, Sec. 4, p. 371.
4. *Ibid.*, Bk. XIV, Sec. 4, pp. 371–74.
5. *Ibid.*, Bk. VII, Sec. 9, p. 189.
6. *Ibid.*, Bk. VI, Sec. 6, p. 147.
7. *Ibid.*
8. *Ibid.*, Bk. IV, Sec. 1, pp. 99–100.
9. *Ibid.*, Bk. VI, Sec. 9, p. 154.
10. *Ibid.*
11. *Ibid.*, Bk. XII, Sec. 3, p. 306. The idea of using medical terms allegorically appealed to a number of writers in the Middle Ages. Cf. Henry of Lancaster, *Le Livre de seyntz medicines*, ed. E. J. Arnould, Anglo-Norman Text Society (Oxford, 1940), and *Cursor mundi* (Vol. III), ed. Richard Morris, EETS, Vols. LXVI, LXVIII (London, 1877, 1878), ll. 27, 382.

theriac.[12] When she wrote the account of her own birth, she said that her father returned from a campaign to find her mother in the pangs of childbirth, and that her mother had made the sign of the cross on her abdomen to postpone the birth of the child until the Emperor should arrive.[13]

The Empress had ordered Anna to be present at the meetings of the physicians attending the Emperor in his last illness "to adjudge the physicians' arguments." When the diagnoses of the case were discussed, Anna sided with Callicles Nicholas, seemingly the only physician whose judgment she valued. He recommended the use of purgatives. The Emperor resembled Chauntecleer in that he "was not accustomed to taking these purgatives; in fact he was quite unaccustomed to drinking medicine."[14] The doctors voted against purging, although Callicles warned them that without purgation the matter would "flow into one of the principal members or into the heart itself, and cause irremediable mischief."[15] They agreed to employ phlebotomy and made an incision at the elbow, in an attempt to relieve the patient's asthmatic breathing.[16] Following that treatment, they tried an "antidote of pepper," which Anna suspected made her father worse by spreading the humors and driving them into the cavities of the arteries.[17] As a last resort, they tried cauterization, but it was to no avail.

Although the treatment of wounds on the battlefield was outside the scope of Anna's own activities, her comments about her father's consideration for his wounded soldiers, his solicitude for his captives, and his wisdom in constructing, upon his return home, a hospital for the ailing, show how extensive were her interests in medical matters. She even included a few words of praise for Duke Robert, her father's enemy, for his consideration of his men. After one engagement the Duke sent for his troops, and dividing them according to race, "enquired from each soldier individually whether he had been seriously wounded or had perhaps received a slight scratch from a sword."[18] But there are few accounts like that of Palaeologus or of Aspietes, who, with a spear piercing his lung and passing out through his spine, fought until he had cleft the helmet and the head of his adversary, and then fell from his horse. "His attendants picked him up, all drained of blood, tended him well and then carried him to the Emperor" to report his bravery.[19] Anna mentioned the baths which were used as one means of healing the wounded and ailing.

12. See *supra*, p. 27.
13. Comnena, *op. cit.*, Bk. VI, Sec. 8, p. 151.
14. *Ibid.*, Bk. XV, Sec. 2, p. 420.   15. *Ibid.*   16. *Ibid.*, Bk. XV, Sec. 11, p. 421.
17. *Ibid.*, Bk. XV, Sec. 11, p. 422.   18. *Ibid.*, Bk. V, Sec. 1, p. 115.
19. *Ibid.*, Bk. XII, Sec. 2, p. 304.

The Contostephani, she related, wishing to avoid a naval battle with Bohemund, pretended that they were ill and "must therefore go to the baths."[20] Alexius, out of sympathy for three hundred counts who had been imprisoned by the Sultan, gave them money and clothing and led them to the baths, "endeavoring in every way to help them recover from their ill treatment."[21]

Anna gave a detailed account of the Emperor's thoughtfulness for the sick and wounded when his army marched homeward with the added impediments of captives and booty.[22] No army before this one had advanced to the music of flutes, in phalanx formation resembling "immovable mountains." The captives, women, and children were enclosed in the center of the ranks of marching soldiers. Expectant mothers presented a special problem. "Since many of the women were with child and many of the men afflicted with disease," Anna explained, "whenever a woman's time for bringing forth came, a trumpet was sounded, at a nod from the Emperor, and made all the men stop and the whole army halted on the instant. And when he knew the child was born, a different call, not the usual one, but provocative of motion, was sounded and stirred them all up to continue the journey."[23] If anyone died, the same procedure was followed. At lunch time the Emperor urged his guests to follow his example by giving the greater part of their victuals to those laboring under illness and old age. He realized the value to the sick of a period of rest and quiet, since the "meal was like a banquet of the gods, for there were no instruments, not even flutes or drums or any disturbing music at all."[24]

When he returned to Constantinople, the Emperor built his remarkable city within a city for the benefit of his captives and guests.[25] Around a large church were houses for the poor and establishments for the maimed and sick. The healthy members of the community ministered to those who were ill. Young people waited upon older members of their own sex. The blind were led by those who could see; babies were nursed by other mothers, if their own were ill; and paralytics were attended by the strong. A prominent citizen acted as guardian of the "orphanage," so called because of the Emperor's "kindness to orphans and to men retired from service."[26]

The Byzantine woman's chief function in the realm of healing, accord-

20. *Ibid.*, Bk. XII, Sec. 8, p. 319.   21. *Ibid.*, Bk. XII, Sec. 1, p. 301.
22. *Ibid.*, Bk. XV, Sec. 7, p. 408.   23. *Ibid.* 24. *Ibid.*
25. *Ibid.*, Bk. XV, Sec. 7, p. 409.   26. *Ibid.*

ing to the chronicle, was to be nurse in the home. She performed alone whatever cures she could, and followed doctors' orders when she needed assistance. Most of the nursing of the Emperor was done by the Empress, whose knowledge must have surpassed that of many professional nurses. When the Emperor once complained of new symptoms, she sent for skilled physicians, ordered them to inquire closely into the nature of his trouble, and then to teach her "the immediate and indirect cause of it."[27] The physicians were certain that the illness could not arise from the Emperor's diet, for under the guidance of the Empress he followed a diet "exceedingly moderate and plain like that of athletes and soldiers. . . ."[28] During his last illness the Empress spent many a sleepless night, "sitting behind him on the bed and supporting him in her arms"[29] in order that she might relieve his difficult breathing. The Princess praised her mother's constant and helpful attentions: "The care she bestowed on him day and night, and the work she did while nursing him and continually changing his position, and devising all kinds of changes in the bedding, these cannot be described." Anna also did her share of the nursing. Because she was so competent, she was slightly contemptuous of the diagnoses and services of the doctors. She was far more satisfied with her own and her mother's efforts to alleviate the distress of the Emperor by taking his pulse, massaging him, and preparing digestible foods for him. Few medieval women were so well read as Anna in academic medicine or so capable of applying what they knew. Three centuries later, Christine de Pisan, daughter of a court astrologer and physician, stands out among medieval writers as the champion of womankind and woman's work. She felt that women did not receive sufficient credit for their contribution to the home and to society, and she expressed her views upon the subject in her literary works. She pointed out the ingratitude of men who criticized women even though women spent their lives as nurses either to their children or to their husbands:

> . . . Dieux, quelles assemblées
> Ou les honneurs des dames sont emblées!
> Et quel proffit vient d'ainssi diffamer
> A ceulz meismes qui se deussent armer
> Pour les garder et leur honneur deffendre?
> Car tout homme doit avoir le cuer tendre
> Envers femme qui a tout homme est mere

27. *Ibid.*, Bk. XV, Sec. 11, p. 421.   28. *Ibid.*   29. *Ibid.*, Bk. XV, Sec. 11, p. 422.

Et ne lui est ne diverse n'amere,
Ançois souefve, doulce et amiable,
A son besoing piteuse et secourable,
Qui tant lui a fait de services,
Et de qui tant les oeuvres sont propices
A corps d'omme souefvement nourrir;
A son maistre, au vivre et au morir,
Lui sont femmes aidans et secourables,
Et piteuses, doulces et serviables.
Si est celui maucognoiscent et rude
Qui en mesdit, et plein d'ingratitude.[30]

With her unusual education and her feeling that women should learn, not only the household arts, but the sciences as well, Christine would scarcely have been the wife for whom the conduct book *Le Ménagier de Paris* was written. The wife of the *bourgeois* of Paris needed instruction even in the simple secrets of household management. Her husband attempted to teach her how to keep her house neat and clean, how to manage her servants, and how to see that they were assigned proper tasks. With great detail he wrote upon the care of furs and clothes and household supplies. His attention was not centered so much upon the work inside the house, however, as upon the activities outside in the garden and upon the recipes for his favorite dishes.

It is obvious that a woman did not write the book, for the section on cookery contains only a few simple remedies for the sick, and in no other

30. Christine de Pisan, "L'Epistre au dieu d'amours," *Oeuvres poétiques de Christine de Pisan*, ed. Maurice Roy, SATF, Vol. XXII, No. 2 (1891), ll. 163–80.

    . . . Heavens, what assemblies
Where the honors of women are stolen!
And what profit comes from thus defaming [women]
To those very persons who ought to arm themselves
To protect them and defend their honor.
For every man ought to have a tender regard
Toward woman, who is a mother to him
And is not changeable or bitter to him,
Always gentle, sweet, and amiable,
To his needs sympathetic and helpful;
Who performs many services for him,
And from whom many deeds are designed
To nurse the body of man tenderly;
To her master, in life and in death,
Woman is helpful and comforting,
Piteous, sweet, and serviceable.
And he is lacking in understanding and is rude,
Who slanders her, and full of ingratitude.

section are other than general remarks made on the subject of their care. A woman of the author's age—some sixty-odd years—writing a guidebook for a young bride about to undertake the responsibilities of a large household in all probability would have devoted a separate article to household remedies. The *bourgeois*, however, as Miss Power observed, was "Epicurus owne sone."[31] His gastronomical interest in the herbs and spices centered upon the marvels which a good cook might produce with them in a poignant sauce, a well-seasoned tart, an herbolace, or a pottage. The aids which he included were not only medicinal, but were also palatable foods for a convalescent. He gave the recipes for five beverages[32] and six pottages for the sick.[33] Since the ingredients were readily obtainable in the Paris shops, the directions could be followed by any cook or housewife. Following are the recipes for two beverages and three pottages for the sick, which Miss Power has translated:

Beverages for the Sick

Tizanne Doulce. Take water and boil it, then for each sester of water put in a bowl heaped with barley, and it matters not if it be hulls and all, and two parisis (2½ d.) worth of liquorice, *item*, figs, and let it be boiled till the barley bursts; then let it be strained through two or three pieces of linen, and in each goblet put great plenty of crystallised sugar. Then the barley is good to give to poultry to eat to fatten them.

Note that the good liquorice is the newest and it is a fresh greenish color, and the old is more faded and dead and is dry.

Bochet. To make six sesters of *bochet* take six pints of very soft honey and set it in a cauldron on the fire, and boil it and stir it for as long as it goes on rising and as long as you see it throwing up liquid in little bubbles which burst and in bursting give off a little blackish steam; and then move it, and put in seven sesters of water and boil them until it is reduced to six sesters, always stirring. And then put it in a tub to cool until it be just warm, and then run it through a sieve, and afterwards put it in a cask and add half a pint of leaven of beer, for it is this which makes it piquant (and if you put in leaven of bread, it is as good for the taste, but the color will be duller), and cover it warmly and well when you prepare it. And if you would make it very good, add thereto an ounce of ginger, long pepper, grain of Paradise and cloves, as much

---

31. *The Goodman of Paris*, ed. and tr. by Eileen Power (New York, 1928), p. 31.
32. *Le Ménagier de Paris, traité de morale et d'économie domestique composé vers 1393 par un bourgeois parisien* (Paris, 1846), II, 237–39.
33. *Ibid.*, II, 241–43.

of the one as of the other, save that there shall be less of the cloves, and put them in a linen bag and cast it therein. And when it hath been therein for two or three days, and the bochet tastes enough of the spices and is sufficiently piquant, take out the bag and squeeze it and put it in the other barrel that you are making. And thus this powder will serve you well two or three times over.[34]

Pottages for the Sick

Flemish Caudle (Chaudeau flament). Set a pot of water to boil, then for each bowl beat up four yolks of eggs with white wine and let it run slowly into your water and stir it very well, and put in salt to the right amount; and when it has well boiled take it from off the fire.

Note. If you are only making one bowl for a sick person you must put in five yolks.

Milk of Almonds. Parboil and peel your almonds and set them in cold water, then bray them and moisten them with water in which onions have been cooked and run through a strainer; then fry the onions and put a little salt therein, and boil it on the fire, and then add sops. And if you are making milk of almonds for the sick, do not put in onions and instead of using water of onions to moisten the almonds as is aforesaid, moisten them with clean warm water and boil it and put in no salt, but plenty of sugar to the drink.

Chicken Mould (Coulis d'un poulet). Cook the chicken until it is all soft, and bray with all its bones in a mortar, then moisten it with its own gravy, strain it and add sugar.

Note that the bones ought to be boiled first, then taken out of the mortar, strained and the mortar cleaned; then bray the meat and great plenty of sugar.

Note that after the great heats of June, spiced pottages come into season, and after St. Remy's Day (Oct. 1st) civey of veal, hare, oysters, etc.[35]

Other remedies in the book were an incantation for the "bite of a dog or other mad beast" and a common one for the toothache. The *bourgeois* believed in the efficacy of charms, and recommended for the bite of a dog that one take a crust of bread and write the following words:

+Bestera +bestie +nay +brigonay +dictera +sagragan +es +domina +fiat +fiat +fiat.[36]

34. *The Goodman of Paris*, pp. 293–94. Cf. *Le Ménagier de Paris*, II, 237–40.
35. *The Goodman of Paris*, pp. 294–95. Cf. *Le Ménagier de Paris*, II, 241–43.
36. *Le Ménagier de Paris*, II, 259.

He did not indicate where the words were to be written. The cure he gave for the toothache was one that was widely used. The instructions were simple:

> Take a covered earthenware pot, or a pot without a lid with a trencher over it, and fill it with water and set it to boil; then undress and go to bed and let your head be well covered, and then take the covered pot and let it be well covered all over, with a hole in the middle or let it be covered with a trencher pierced in the middle. And hold your teeth against the hole, with your mouth wide open, in order to breathe the steam of the water passing through the hole, and let sage and other herbs be set therein and keep yourself well covered up.[37]

The hot vapor was doubtless more helpful than many a remedy to be found in the scientific works of the century.[38]

The *bourgeois* thought that two other simple directions in the matter of illness were sufficient for his young wife. Maintaining the high moral tone of conduct books in general, which usually attempted to formulate a perfect pattern of life, he derived his first bit of advice from the religious precept that the fourth branch of mercy was to visit the sick.[39] The second admonition was practical and specific. He stated his wife's obligations toward her servants in the event of illness: ". . . if one of your servants fall ill, do you lay all common concerns aside, and do you yourself take thought for him full lovingly and kindly, and visit him and think of him or her very carefully, seeking to bring about his cure."[40] The housewife's first responsibility, in his opinion, clearly lay in the care of her household; her next concern was to engage in charitable works.

The comments on the subject of sickness made by the Paston ladies in their letters were much more explicit than the remarks of the *bourgeois*. When the Paston men were ill, they wrote to the women at home for advice; and the letters in reply told what measures should be taken. The women exchanged remedies with each other and with their friends, experimented with them, and passed them on to their neighbors. In cases of severe illness, they summoned physicians, with whose services

---

37. *The Goodman of Paris*, p. 304. Cf. *Le Ménagier de Paris*, II, 257.
38. Cf., for example, the suggestions of Lanfranc in his *Science of Cirurgie* (ed. Robert V. Fleischhacker, EETS, CII [1894], 264) which conclude with the recommendation that for the ache which comes from "vices" of the head or gums, caused by heat, the patient should be bled in the "head veins" and in the vein under the tongue. He should then hold either oil of roses or cold water and vinegar in his mouth.
39. *Le Ménagier de Paris*, I, 58.
40. *Ibid.*, II, 71–72.

they were not always pleased. Their experience was that of the typical intelligent housewife, upon whose ministrations the physical welfare of the family depended.

Agnes and Margaret Paston were not so well educated as Anna Comnena, but they were no less intelligent than she was in the management of family affairs. They lacked Anna's classical training, and their knowledge of medicine came from neighbors, apothecaries, and books of physic of the type which Sir John had copied for them. Yet their letters reflect the same natural interest in the illnesses of their families, and perhaps show more warmth of feeling than Anna did. On September 28, 1443, Margaret wrote to John:

> Ryth worchipful hosbon, I recommande me to yow, desyryng hertely to her of your wilfar, thanckyng God of yowr a mendyng of the grete dysese that ye have hade: and I thancke yow for the letter that ye sent me, for be my trowthe my moder and I wer nowth [not] in hertys es [heart's ease] fro the tyme that we woste of yowr sekenesse, tyl we woste verely of yowr a mendyng. . . Yf I mythe might have had my wylle, I xulde a seyne yow er dystyme [should have seen you ere this time]; I wolde ye wern at hom, yf it were your ese, and your sor myth ben as wyl lokyth to her as it tys there ye ben [sore might be as well looked to here as it is where ye be], now lever dan a goune zow [though] it wer of scarlette.[41]

The differences in the lives and times of the Comnena and the Paston women account for some of the divergences in their beliefs and nursing practices. An empress and a princess at the imperial court in Constantinople, Irene and Anna Comnena could always turn to the royal physicians for the best advice then available. Women of the English upper middle class, living in Norfolk, Agnes, Margaret, and Margery Paston were obliged to rely mainly upon their own abilities to heal the sick at home. If the Paston men became ill in London, where they were frequently engaged in business, they consulted physicians there. If the Paston women were seriously ill at home, there was nothing to do but to send for a doctor from a neighboring village and await his coming. The management of a large household of relatives and servants required all the Paston women to play the rôles of nurse and physician in caring for children, bandaging wounds, setting bones, and treating colds and other complaints. Herbal medicine and cures in the convenient forms of ointments, plasters, and potions composed some of the remedies mentioned in the Paston letters.

41. *The Paston Letters*, ed. James Gairdner (London, 1900–1901), Letter, No. 36.

The Paston cures did not consist wholly of these medicaments, however. The postscript of Margaret Paston's letter to John contained advice that reflected the constant emphasis in medieval times upon diet as a cure. "My modyr grette yow wel, and sendyth yow Goddys blyssyng and hers," she added, "and sche prayeth yow, and I pray yow also, that ye be wel dyetyd of mete and drynke, for that is the grettest helpe that ye may have now to your helthe ward." The Pastons also believed that polluted air was the cause of disease, a common theory from the time of the first appearance of the plague. Margaret wrote to John, asking him to send her "a booke wyth chardeqweyns," a preserve made of quinces, that she might use it in the mornings, "for the eyeres [airs] be nat holsom in this town."[42]

Since the Paston women liked to keep up with the times, some of the most interesting topics in their letters were the errands upon which they sent their husbands and sons in London. If they did not want a piece of ribbon or some cloth for a dress, they asked for fruit or spices that were unobtainable in the shops nearer home. They also made requests for medicinal supplies or those to be used, like the quince preserves, as preventive remedies. On June 3, 1451, Margaret sent word to John, reminding him to buy the "ungwentum album,"[43] a popular ointment. A month later she wrote again to John: "I pray yow hertyly that ye woll send me a potte with treacle in hast; for I have been rygth evyll att ese, and your dowghter bothe, syth that ye yeden hens [since ye went hence], and one of the tallest younge men of this parysch lyth syke and hath a grete myrr [cold]. How he shall do God knowyth."[44] "Treacle," which was being imported from Genoa, was in great demand by the Paston

---

42. *Ibid.*, Letter No. 182. Quince marmalade is mentioned also in John Russell's "Boke of Nurture" (ed. F. J. Furnivall in *Early English Meals and Manners*, EETS, Vol. XXXII [1868], l. 72). Russell did not associate the preserves with the plague. See Furnivall's Index *s.v.* "Chardequynce."

43. *The Paston Letters*, Letter No. 163. George Henslow, *Medical Works of the Fourteenth Century* (London, 1899), pp. 78–79, gives the following recipe for the "ungwentum album":
"Take halfe an vnce of mastik, of litarge, and scome of siluer, and of gold iiii peny wyghte, of blank plum [white lead] ii vnces, of ceruse half an vnce, and grynd alle thyse to-gedere on a peynteres ston with a moline [mill] In-to small poudere, and thanne take whyt vynegre or ellis red and do into the poudre on the ston, and make thikke must. In gryndyng al wele to-gedere, and put in a litil oyle of (o) lyf and grynd alle wele togedere, and thanne droppe In whytes of egges wel beten and clere scomed as any water and alwey grynde fore togedere as peynteres grynde here coloures, and do so ofte tymes as ye deden by-fore with the vynnegre and with oyle and with whitis of the eggis, til it be as thynne as chyldes pap and put it in boxis and kep it to youre vs. This oynement must be mad in an hot sonne and is good for saucefleume, and for scaldyng and for brennyng . . ."

44. *The Paston Letters*, Letter No. 167.

family and seems to have been one of the most trusted remedies in the family medicine cabinets. John mentioned it to Margaret in 1462 (?):

> Please it you to weet that I send you by Barker, the bearer hereof, three treacle pots of Geane as my Apothecary sweareth unto me, and moreover that they were never undone since they came from Geane, whereof ye shall take as many as pleaseth you, nevertheless, my Brother John[45] sent to me for two, therefore I must beseech you that he may have at least one. . .[46]

John continued to identify the pots, telling Margaret which one he thought had been opened and which one he thought was best. "Treacle" was considered good medicine for the plague, for in the same letter in which he reports the numerous deaths from the plague in Norwich in 1479, John asked his brother, Sir John, to send him two pots of "treacle" by the next messenger.[47]

The Paston men placed great faith in the advice and the medicines of the women of their family. Both Agnes and Margaret were strong-minded women and maintained control over the affairs of their sons even after they were married. While Sir John was suffering from a pain in his heel on one of his sojourns in London, his mother (Margaret) must have urged him to leave London. He dutifully agreed: "and where ye advised me to hasten out of this town, I would full fain be hence."[48] Some years later the younger Sir John sent a hurried appeal to his wife, Margery:

> I prey yow in all hast possybyll to send me, by the next swer [sure] messenger that ye can gete, a large playster of your *flose ungwentorum* for Kynges Attorney, Jamys Hobart, for all hys dysease is but an ache in hys knee. He is the man that brought yow and me togedyrs, and I had lever than xl *li.* ye koud with your playster depart hym and hys peyne. But when ye send me the playster, ye myst send me wryght-yng hough it shold be leyd to and takyn from hys knee, and hough longe it shold abyd on hys knee unrenevyd, and hough longe the playster wyll laste good, and whethyr he must lape eny more clothys about the playster to kepe it warme or nought.[49]

We can only conclude that Margery's plaster had wrought wonders at

---

45. Two sons were christened John, and one bore the title "Sir John."
46. *The Paston Letters*, Letter No. 563.   47. *Ibid.*, Letter No. 841.
48. *Ibid.*, Letter No. 212.   49. *Ibid.*, Letter No. 898.

home, for otherwise Sir John would not have recommended it to so prominent a man as the King's attorney.

Comments in the *Paston Letters* on the pestilence show the same helplessness in coping with the plague that prevailed everywhere in Italy, France, and England. With every visitation of it people attempted to fly from the cities and towns to the country. So "fervent" was it at Norwich in 1465 that Elizabeth Clere fled to Ormesby and Agnes Paston to Caister.[50] In 1471, however, Margaret wrote to her younger son John of the pestilence raging in the neighboring villages, and added: "all thys hwlsold [household] and thys parych ys as ye leftyd [left it], blyssyd be Gode. We lewyn in fer [live in fear], but we wut nat qweder [wot not whether] to fle, for to be better than we ben here."[51] Evidently concerned over the possibility of a long confinement at home, Margaret composed a list of supplies that she would need. She sent money to John for sugar and dates, and asked him to send her the prices of pepper, cloves, mace, ginger, cinnamon, almonds, rice, galangal, saffron, and currants so that she could buy them wherever they were cheapest.[52] In 1479, a few days before Sir John was seized with the plague, his younger brother, John, wrote asking him for two pots of Genoan treacle. People were dying everywhere about him, he stated, but his "wyff" and his "women" did not come out of the house and had no place to which they could flee.[53] In August, 1479, Walter, a younger son of Margaret, died of the plague, and on November 15 his older brother John was taken. So often and so devastatingly did the pestilence strike the Paston neighborhood that there was no time to write in the letters of medicines, much less to administer them. In any case, all medicines failed.

Upon occasion, the Paston men were requested to send a doctor for someone at home. Agnes, in 1444, sent a message to her husband, praying him to remember her green ginger of almonds for Lent and the leech at Orwell, for her sickness had increased daily, and she was "sore a ferd."[54] One sympathizes with her for her long wait while the message was first delivered to William and then relayed to the doctor, and while the doctor rode on horseback from Orwell to Paston. Sometimes people were thoughtful enough to offer to their friends the services of doctors who were attending them, as in the case of the friend who wrote to Margaret: "Mastres, my Lady sent to Cawmbrygg for a doctour of fesyk.

50. *Ibid.*, Letter No. 523.   51. *Ibid.*, Letter No. 681.
52. *Ibid.*   53. *Ibid.*, Letter No. 841.   54. *Ibid.*, Letter No. 38.

If ye wyll ony thyng with hym, he xal abyde this daye and to morwe.
He is ryght a konnyng man and gentyll."[55]

In many cases of sudden illness in the Middle Ages, even the immediate
assistance of doctors was of no avail. Diseases which today tax the skill
of the most advanced medical men were obviously beyond the powers of
medieval healers, and then as now, they often caused sudden death.
Sir John Hevenyngham's was typical of hundreds of such cases. "His
sickness," Margaret wrote, "toke him on Tewsday, at ix [nine] of the
clok before none, and be too [by two] after none he was dedd."[56]

The experience of the Paston family with doctors led the women to
become as skeptical as Anna Comnena of any real benefit to be derived
from their ministrations. Margaret, especially, seems to have felt that
it was far safer to trust to popular remedies than to consult a doctor,
particularly in London. Her very decided feeling in the matter of professional aid is expressed in a letter to her husband, written June 8, 1464.
"Also for Goddys sake," she warned him, "be war what medesyns ye
take of any fysissyans of London: I schal never trust to hem because
of your fadir and myn onkyl, whoys sowlys God assoyle."[57]

This lack of faith in the ability of physicians to cure all ailments combined with other factors to turn the housewife's attention to growing a
large garden of herbs and learning to concoct her remedies from her own
supplies and those she could obtain from an apothecary shop. The dis-
advantages and dangers of waiting in small towns and villages for doctors
to come from larger centers were obvious. Moreover, the housewife knew
that she could imitate the doctor and heal most of the ailments of her
household with plasters and potions similar to his.

IN FICTION

The medical work of the lay women in the romances and *chansons de
geste* reflected the knowledge and practice of women like the Pastons,
the wife of the Parisian *bourgeois*, and, in some instances, the Princess
Anna. Like these, the women healers in fiction were especially skilled in
the use of herbal medicines and in the care of wounds.

The accounts of the healing which took place in fiction, however, were
governed by several literary requirements. In romances, lais, and *chansons de geste*, in particular, the themes were mainly love and adventure,
neither of which could progress far with heroes incapacitated or easily
overcome by their foes. Knightly heroes who were wounded had to be

55. *Ibid.*, Letter No. 432.   56. *Ibid.*, Letter No. 189.   57. *Ibid.*, Letter No. 490.

cured, frequently with miraculous celerity, so that skirmishes, combats, and campaigns could end in glorious victory. Furthermore, unlike actual experience, the efforts of the healer had to be consistently successful.

Conventional practice, both in fiction and among most housewives in the later Middle Ages, accounts for the fact that methods of healing varied little from the twelfth to the sixteenth century. In actual life, as we have seen, herbal medicine remained the constant means of cure throughout this period, and except for using new unguents or compounds, like the "treacle" from Genoa, which apothecaries sold, most women failed to keep pace with the discoveries made by progressive physicians and surgeons. The romances were not concerned with presenting an appreciation of medieval science such as the Princess Anna with her unusual education possessed, but rather with healing a knight's wounds quickly with remedies acceptable to all readers. And since traditional methods of healing linger even for centuries after scientific progress has outmoded them, there was every reason why Lillias in the fifteenth-century romance *Eger and Grime* resorted to the same procedure in healing wounds that the sisters of Guivret followed in Chrétien's twelfth-century *Erec et Enide*. For this reason it is fruitless to present a study of healing in the romances in chronological order. More to the point is a study of the knowledge and qualifications of the women entrusted with the cures, and the methods they used in effecting them.

Neither women nor men appeared in the role of healer in fiction unless they were reputed to have some skill in healing. Josian, in *Beves of Hampton*, had learned both physic and surgery from masters of Bologna and Toledo.[58] In Malory's *Morte Darthur*, the Irish king placed Tantris in the care of his daughter, La Belle Iseult, "because she was a noble surgion."[59] The daughter of the king in the ballad "Sir Cawline" was called "a leeche full ffine."[60] Aigline, whose ministrations revive and cure Gerart in *Le Roman de la Violette*, was described as one "ki molt fu sage."[61] The sisters of Guivret, who added their services to those of Enide in curing Erec's wounds, were complimented when their brother declared that "mout sevent de garir plaies."[62] King Finlac's daughter,

58. *Beves of Hampton*, ed. Eugen Kölbing, EETS, Vols. XLVI, XLVIII, LXXV (1894), ll. 3671–76.
59. Sir Thomas Malory, *Le Morte Darthur*, ed. H. Oskar Sommer (London, 1889), Bk. II, Chap. IX.
60. "Sir Cawline," *The English and Scottish Popular Ballads*, ed. Francis James Child (Boston, 1882–98), II, 8, 61.
61. Gerbert de Montreuil, *Le Roman de la Violette*, ed. Douglas L. Buffum, SATF, Vol. LXXXI (1928), l. 2109.
62. Kristian von Troyes, *Erec und Enide*, ed. Wendelin Foerster (Halle, 1890), l. 5112.

Acula, in *Horn Childe*, was "sleiʒe" of wounds.[63] The skill of his daughter made Triṣtram, in *L'Atre périlleux*, boast of her accomplishments.[64] And Melior, in *Partonope of Blois*, was also remarkable for her education in medicine. In giving an account of her training, she stated that she had learned the seven sciences, and knew the virtues of herbs and roots, and whether they were hot or cold. She could easily heal the sick.[65] In Gottfried von Strassburg's *Tristan*, Morholt boasted that his sister, Queen Isolt, was the only person in the country who could cure Tristram.[66] Floripas, in *Fierabras*, had the same faith in the outcome of her ministrations:

Par foi, ce dist la bele, je vous donrai santé.[67]

In *Gaufrey*,[68] Fauquette asked to heal Robastre, and in *König Dietrich von Bern*,[69] Helche, King Etzel's queen, begged for the same privilege when Dietrich was wounded. And in *A Royal Historie of the Excellent Knight Generides*,[70] Clarionas used the boast that she knew the "virtues of grasse and of rotes" as a ruse to gain access to Generides.

If a knight was wounded, he was usually removed from the field of combat to a castle, hostel, or religious house. There his armor was removed, usually by an attendant, but frequently by the person who was to give him medical care. If a woman was to attend him, she took off his heavy armor, for she could then examine his wounds. Thus following the custom Aigline disarmed Gerart,[71] Blonde quickly disarmed Jehan in *Jehan et Blonde*,[72] and Enide rendered the same service to Erec.[73] With the assistance of a squire, Odelis disarmed Meraugis, in *Meraugis de Portlesquez*,[74] after feeling his heart-beat. In *Richars li Beaus*,[75] Clarisse, the mother of Richard, wept as she divested her son of his gory clothes.

63. *Horn Childe*, ed. Joseph Hall (Oxford, 1901), Appendix, l. 792.
64. *L'Atre périlleux*, ed. Brian Woledge (Paris, 1936), ll. 6310 ff.
65. *Partonope of Blois*, ed. A. Trampe Bödtker, EETS, Vol. CIX (1912), ll. 5919 ff.
66. Gottfried von Strassburg, *Tristan*, ed. Friedrich Ranke (Berlin, 1930), ll. 6948 ff.
67. *Fierabras*, ed. A. Kroeber and G. Servais, APF, Vol. IV (1860), l. 2208.
68. *Gaufrey*, ed. F. Guessard and P. Chabaille, APF, Vol. III (1859), ll. 3920–21.
69. *König Dietrich von Bern*, ed. Ernst Martin (Halle, 1867), pp. 132–33.
70. *A Royal Historie of the Excellent Knight Generides*, ed. Frederick J. Furnivall (Hertford, 1865), l. 9921.
71. Gerbert de Montreuil, *op. cit.*, ll. 2110–11.
72. Philippe de Rémi, "Jehan et Blonde," in *Oeuvres poétiques de Philippe de Rémi* (Tome II), ed. Hermann Suchier, SATF, Vol. XVII (1885), l. 4449.
73. Kristian von Troyes, *op. cit.*, l. 5132.
74. Raoul von Houdenc, *Meraugis von Portlesquez*, ed. Mathias Friedwagner (Halle, 1897), ll. 4695–86.
75. *Richars li Beaus*, ed. Wendelin Foerster (Vienna, 1874), ll. 2923 ff.

Hector, in the *Roman de Troie*,[76] was attended by his mother and his sisters, who first removed his helm, then his hauberk, then his kneepieces. Gyburc disarmed Willehalm, in Wolfram von Eschenbach's *Willehalm*,[77] whereas Lynet managed this cumbersome task alone in the *Morte Darthur*[78] for both Sir Beaumains and the Red Knight of the Red Launds. Because the armor was very heavy, women sometimes assisted each other in removing it. Three maidens, for example, in *Otinel*,[79] took off Ogier's armor. "Ladyes and damoysels" disarmed Ewain, Gawain, and Marhaus in Malory's *Morte Darthur*[80] and "hastely loked to theyr hurtes," when the three rode to Marhaus's priory. Two maids removed Sir Eger's bloody armor, in *Eger and Grime*,[81] so that Lillias, the Fairy Lady, might "search his wounds."

The steps followed in healing wounds were usually those outlined in *The Siege of Jerusalem*, at the time when a large number of Romans were wounded:

> Leches by torch-liȝt: loken her hurtes,
> Waschen woundes with wyn: & with wolle stoppen,
> With oyle & orisoun; ordeyned in charme.[82]

After the knight had been disarmed and his injuries examined, his wounds had to be cleansed and dressed. In general, these procedures followed actual medical practice, but the details of some of the accounts were clearly chosen for entertainment and not for instruction. Many of the descriptions of the cleansing and dressing of the wounds are as brief as that of Enide's first-aid treatment of Erec:

> Si li a ses plaies lavees
> Ressuiiees et rebandees.[83]

Erec was taken to Guivret's sisters for further aid, however, for they were more skilled in medicine than Enide.[84] In the *Roman de Troie*[85] during Hector's illness, Helen gently washed his wounds. Gold or silver

76. Benoît de Sainte-More, *Le Roman de Troie*, ed. Léopold Constans, SATF, Vol. II (1904–12), ll. 10,219 ff.
77. Wolfram von Eschenbach, *Willehalm*, ed. Karl Lachmann (3d. ed.; Berlin, 1872), Sec. II, p. 99, ll. 20 ff.
78. Malory, *op. cit.*, Bk. VII, Chap. XVIII.
79. *Otinel*, ed. F. Guessard and H. Michelant, APF, Vol. I (1859), ll. 1045–46.
80. Malory, *op. cit.*, Bk. IV, Chap. XVIII.
81. *Eger and Grime*, ed. James Ralston Caldwell, "Harvard Studies in Comparative Literature," Vol. IX (Cambridge, 1933), Percy MS, l. 243.
82. *The Siege of Jerusalem*, ed. Eugen Kölbing and Mabel Day, EETS, Vol. CLXXXVIII (1932), ll. 855–57.
83. Kristian von Troyes, *op. cit.*, ll. 5133 f.
84. *Ibid.*, ll. 5111–13, 5201.
85. Benoît de Sainte-More, *op. cit.*, ll. 14,619 ff.

basins were often employed for this purpose. The beautiful young wife and her attendant who waited upon Guigemar, in the lai of "Guigemar"[86] by Marie de France, brought basins of gold in which to bathe his wounds.

Some of the romances and *chansons de geste* stipulated the degree of warmth as well as the kind of liquid to be used in washing the wounds, and thus added a touch of realism. Blonde employed clear water and tepid wine in caring for Jehan's wounds.[87] Lillias cleansed Sir Eger's hand with warm water brought in a silver basin.[88] In treating the wounds of Tydeüs, the daughter of Lycurgus used a mixture of claret, some "piment" [an aromatic wine], and salt.[89]

Removing the dead flesh from the wound was an important step often mentioned in medical directions for treatment of wounds. Lanfranc[90] and Guy de Chauliac[91] stressed the need for this careful cleansing so that the wound might heal thoroughly. The sisters of Guivret took the precaution of cutting away the dead flesh before they applied a plaster to Erec's wound.[92] Wounds so treated usually responded immediately and took on a healthier appearance.

After being cleansed, many of the wounds were tented, a practice of dilating a natural canal with a roll of linen in order to keep open the orifice of the wound. Guivret's sisters followed this treatment.[93] A damsel carefully tented Durmart's wound, in *Durmart li Gallois*,[94] and Lillias "stopped" that of Sir Eger "full of silk."[95] The following day, Lillias continued her ministrations, which Sir Eger described:

> "The bloody tents away she drew,
> And tented me again with new:
> The tents that in my wounds yeed,
> Trust ye well they were no threed.
> They were neither lake nor line,
> Of silk they were both good and fine,
> The mistenting of my wounds,
> Cost that Lady twenty pounds."[96]

86. Marie de France, "Guigemar," in *Die Lais der Marie de France*, ed. Karl Warnke (Halle, 1900), ll. 369–70.
87. Philippe de Rémi, *op. cit.*, l. 4451.
88. *Eger and Grime*, Percy MS, ll. 249 ff.; Huntington MS, ll. 295–96.
89. *Le Roman de Thèbes*, ed. Léopold Constans, SATF, Vol. XXX¹ (Paris, 1890), ll. 2813–15.
90. Lanfranc, *op. cit.*, CII, 34, 38, 122 ff.
91. Guy de Chauliac, *La Grande Chirurgie*, ed. E. Nicaise (Paris, 1890), pp. 208–9.
92. Kristian von Troyes, *op. cit.*, l. 5198.
93. *Ibid.*, l. 5199.
94. *Durmart li Gallois*, ed. Edmund Stengel, Bibliothek des literarische Vereins Stuttgart, Vol. CXVI (Tübingen, 1873), l. 3168.
95. *Eger and Grime*, Huntington MS, l. 324.
96. *Ibid.*, Percy MS, ll. 277 ff.

Available cloths, shirts or blouses, pennons, or flags supplied the materials for bandages. The women attending Guigemar used a fine white cloth made of flax for a bandage;[97] whereas Odelis, nursing Meraugis, took a white sleeve to dry the wound.[98] A bandage of "pale," a silk imported from Alexandria, served for Alexander's wounds in *Li Romans d' Alixandre*,[99] and one of "porpre," a heavy material, for those of Emmenidus d'Arcade in the same romance.[100] For Aucassin's dislocated shoulder Nicolette tore off the hem of her chemise.[101] Perceval "stopped his bledyng wounde with a pyece of his sherte,"[102] when he chastised himself through flagellation. The daughter of Lycurgus used on Tydeüs's wounds four bandages of orphrey, a richly embroidered cloth.[103]

In accordance with the customary practice in everyday life, wounds in medieval fiction were also tightly bandaged. John Arderne was one of the few doctors who advocated leaving the wound open to heal;[104] the general practice in professional and popular medicine was to bandage it tightly and to change the bandage often. Guigemar firmly bandaged his wound himself, before the women who attended him dressed it in the same way.[105] Hector's wounds were bandaged tightly,[106] as were those of Meraugis[107] and of the men fighting the Saracens with Aymeri de Narbonne.[108] In actual practice, the tight bandaging must have caused acute suffering. In the *Roman de la Violette*[109] Gerart was bandaged so securely by Aigline that he suffered extreme pain.

The same healing powers attributed to a cure or to a physician in professional practice were ascribed in fiction to the contents of a prescription or to a skilled man or woman. No greater aura of fame surrounded Galen, Guy de Chauliac, or John Arderne and their medicines in actual life than was attached to Morgan le Fay in fiction. Like Arderne's valence of wormwood[110] and the potion called "sage,"[111] in which people

97. Marie de France, *op. cit.*, ll. 371–72.
98. Raoul von Houdenc, *op. cit.*, ll. 4736–37.
99. Lambert li Tors and Alexandre de Bernay, *Li Romans d'Alixandre*, ed. Heinrich Michelant, BLV, Vol. XIII (Stuttgart, 1846), l. 28.
100. *Ibid.*, l. 10.
101. *Aucassin et Nicolette*, ed. Mario Roques (2d. ed.; Paris, 1936), Sec. XXVI, l. 14.
102. Malory, *op. cit.*, Bk. XIV, Chap. X.
103. *Le Roman de Thèbes*, ll. 2818–20.
104. John Arderne, *Treatises of Fistula in Ano*, ed. Sir D'Arcy Power, EETS, Vol. CXXXIX (1910), 100.
105. Marie de France, *op. cit.*, ll. 141–42, 373.
106. Benoît de Sainte-More, *op. cit.*, ll. 10,095–96.
107. Raoul von Houdenc, *op. cit.*, ll. 4740–42.
108. *Aymeri de Narbonne*, ed. Louis Demaison, SATF, Vol. XXIV (1887), l. 4284.
109. Gerbert de Montreuil, *op. cit.*, l. 2127.
110. Made of absinth, parsley, plantain, and swine's grease. Arderne, *op. cit.*, p. 98.
111. See *supra*, p. 28.

placed great faith, the plasters of Morgan, in *Erec et Enide*, could heal all kinds of wounds.[112] If the healer were not so well known as the famous fay, however, emphasis was thrown upon the treatment. Depending upon the supplies on hand, the healer selected a bath, a plaster, a potion, a salve, or a particular herb for its beneficial qualities and gave it the credit for the cure.

Many injuries requiring medical attention were speedily healed by means of baths, in which herbs were steeped. We have already had occasion to observe Tristram taking a medicinal tub. Clarisse prepared such a bath with which to heal her son Richard's wounds.[113] Guivret's sisters restored Erec's healthy color by means of a bath.[114] Lancelot, as we have noted, used the pretense of sending Elaine to the forest to gather herbs for his bath, in Malory's *Morte Darthur*.[115] In Chrétien's *Lancelot*,[116] the sister of Meleagant resuscitated Lancelot by bathing and massaging him. A bath was prepared for Parzival while he slept.[117]

The healing "par herbe et par emplastre et par bone puison" mentioned in *Li Romans d'Alixandre*[118] suggests that herbs, plasters, and potions were the chief medicines administered to the wounded knights. With the bath and the ointment, these may be said to represent the major possibilities of the amateur woman's medical treatment. These remedies were sometimes used singly, sometimes in combination with others. The daughter of Lycurgus anointed Tydeüs with a balm.[119] In Chrétien's *Lancelot*, King Baudemagus offered Lancelot the hospitality of his castle and promised to secure some "oignement as trois Maries"[120] and even something better, if it could be found, to heal the cuts Lancelot had received while crossing the sword-bridge. Foerster noted that the naming of the salve followed both Biblical and medieval traditions and that the three Marys are the saints Mary Magdalen, Mary, the mother of James, and Mary Salome.[121] In *Les Merveilles de Rigomer*, the fay Lorie cured Lancelot's burns with a special ointment which she took out of a little ivory box and rubbed on his head and neck, shoulders, and arms.[122]

112. Kristian von Troyes, *op. cit.*, ll. 4217–226.
113. *Richars li Beaus*, ll. 2937–38.
114. Kristian von Troyes, *op. cit.*, ll. 5220 ff.
115. Malory, *op. cit.*, Bk. XVIII, Chap. XVII.
116. Kristian von Troyes, *Der Karrenritter*, ed. Wendelin Foerster (Halle, 1899), l. 6683.
117. Wolfram von Eschenbach, *Parzival und Titurel*, ed. Ernst Martin (Halle, 1900), Sec. III, p. 167, ll. 1 ff.
118. Lambert li Tors and Alexandre de Bernay, *op. cit.*, l. 32.
119. *Le Roman de Thèbes*, l. 2817.
120. Kristian von Troyes, *Der Karrenritter*, ll. 3374–75.
121. *Ibid.*, note to l. 3324, p. 389.
122. *Les Mervelles de Rigomer par Jehan* (Vol. I), ed. Wendelin Foerster, Gesellschaft für Romanische Literatur, Vol. XIX (1908), ll. 16,955 ff.

So swift was its action that some thought that Lorie was the Magdalen herself, with her precious ointment. Enfamy, in *Otuel and Roland*, applied herself day and night to the care of Ogier, "gaf hym drynkes der," and "made hym salues soft."[123] When Fenice, in *Cligés*, was maltreated by some Salernitan doctors, Thessala came to her rescue with "un mout precieus oignemant."[124] Acula was asked by her father, King Finlac, in *Horn Childe*, to make a plaster for Horn.[125] Guivret's sisters applied new plasters to Erec's wounds after each washing.[126] Aigline employed a combination of a plaster and an ointment "as clear as oil and made into treacle," which could heal the largest wounds.[127] Floripas healed Oliver with a little mandragora, which took immediate effect.[128] With the aid of dittany, Gyburc stanched the blood of Willehalm's wound.[129] Rosamonde, in *Elie de Saint Gille*, used nine herbs in a potion which she mixed for Elie, and then prepared a bath for him.[130] Three maidens gave Ogier an "herbe duce" to eat, after which he slept to awaken refreshed.[131] Sir Eger told Sir Grime that in dressing his wounds, the fairy lady, Lillias, used spices, salves, and herbs along with the grass-green fairy drink.[132] The maiden who attended Durmart restored him to health with a potion and an ointment.[133] Tristram's daughter took an herb of great virtue called "toscane" and bound it on Gawain's wound.[134] To heal Robastre's bruises, Fauquette took an herb of "grant bonte," ground it, and infused it in a potion.[135] Since the herb was endowed with the virtue of healing as soon as it passed down the throat, Robastre immediately became as "healthy as an apple." He was overjoyed at the prompt results of the treatment and expressed his gratitude:

> "Benoite soit la dame qui tele me donna
> Et la terre ensement qui tele herbe porta."[136]

123. *Firumbras and Otuel and Roland*, ed. Mary Isabelle O'Sullivan, EETS, Vol. CXCVIII (1935), ll. 1016–19.
124. Kristian von Troyes, *Cligés*, ed. Wendelin Foerster (Halle, 1884), ll. 6064 ff.
125. *Horn Childe*, l. 791.
126. Kristian von Troyes, *Erec und Enide*, l. 5203.
127. Gerbert de Montreuil, *op. cit.*, ll. 2218–22; 2123–25.
128. *Fierabras*, ll. 2209 ff. Cf. *The Lyf of the Nobel and Crysten Prynce, Charles the Grete*, tr. William Caxton, ed. Sidney J. H. Herrtage, EETS, Vols. XXXVI–XXXVII (1881), l. 95.
129. Wolfram von Eschenbach, *Willehalm*, Sec. II, p. 99, ll. 20 ff. Wolfram adds here that flowers are also good for stanching blood, Sec. II, p. 99, l. 29.
130. *Elie de Saint Gille*, ed. Gaston Raynaud, SATF, Vol. XII (1879), ll. 1459 ff.
131. *Otinel*, ll. 1050 ff. An herb is referred to in *Beves of Hampton* (ll. 2301–08), which, mixed with Rhenish wine, would make a man sleep a day and a night.
132. *Eger and Grime*, Percy MS, l. 285.
133. *Durmart li Gallois*, ll. 3171–76; 3184–85.
134. *L'Atre périlleux*, ll. 6328–30.
135. *Gaufrey*, l. 3928.
136. *Ibid.*, ll. 3935–36.

Only a slight reflection of the general medieval emphasis upon diet as a preventive measure or as a road to health is found in the medical practices of women healers in fiction. Although laymen as well as doctors quoted widely the lines regarding diet from the *Regimen sanitatis Salernitatum*,[137] diet did not play a prominent part in the medieval cure of wounds and therefore it is only rarely mentioned. The principal application of the "measurable diet" of which Chaucer's physician approved was abstinence from pepper and garlic while wounds were healing. Aigline gave Gerart food and drink but permitted no pepper or garlic in his diet.[138] Four or five times a day Guivret's sisters gave Erec nourishment, but they also banned pepper and garlic from the menu.[139] It is interesting to note in this connection that Princess Anna Comnena had wondered whether her father had not been made worse by an antidote of pepper which the doctors gave him in his last illness.[140]

In the process of healing wounds in medieval fiction, the time required for the cure supplies the most unrealistic of details. Recuperation might take place immediately, or extend over a period of twelve months. The mandragora which Floripas gave Oliver cured him as soon as he had used it.[141] The author of *Elie de Saint Gille* tells us that God did not make the man who was not as well "as a fish in water" when he swallowed the medicine which Rosamonde compounded for Elie.[142] On the other hand, it took Dawntower, in *Sir Eglamour of Artois*, a year to cure Eglamour of a deep wound inflicted by a dragon.[143] One suspects that an easy rime sometimes determined the time element in healing. The poet about to state that Beves was made "both hol and sonde" would naturally think that his health returned within "a lite stonde."[144] Chrétien de Troyes may have determined the time of Erec's convalescence by the same exigencies that ruled the choice of words:

> A lui garir mistrent tel painne
> Les puceles, qu'einçois quinzainne
> Ne santi il mal ne dolor.[145]

A more realistic note is found in the concern of kings over the welfare

137. See *supra*, p. 22.
138. Gerbert de Montreuil, *op. cit.*, ll. 2137–39.
139. Kristian von Troyes, *Erec und Enide*, ll. 5204–06.
140. See *supra*, p. 39.
141. *Fierabras*, l. 2210.
142. *Elie de Saint Gille*, ll. 1450–51.
143. "Sir Eglamour of Artois," in *The Early English Romances* . . ., ed. James Orchard Halliwell, Camden Society, Vol. XXX (1844), ll. 769–71.
144. *Beves of Hampton*, ll. 733–34.
145. Kristian von Troyes, *Erec und Enide*, ll. 5217–19.

of their armies. Neither the Emperor Alexius nor Robert Guiscard took the health of his army more to heart than did the legendary Arthur; for in the romances, the British king often summoned leeches to attend to the injuries of his knights.[146] King Mark also took a personal interest in Tristram's case, when the wound could not be healed. He sent after "alle maner of leches & surgens bothe unto men and wymmen. . ."[147]

The activities of the women in nursing services near the battlefields of the crusaders are rarely mentioned in the romances or the *chansons de geste*. Individual men and women performed innumerable medical services for the heroes injured in battle, but those women who carried water or brought first aid to the men after a skirmish received little attention, possibly because they were accepted as a matter of course. In his account of the capture of Jerusalem, Graindor de Douai described one scene in which a group of women were working together. After the army halted and the wounded were carried off the field, the women advanced to bring some relief from suffering.

> Iluec vinrent les dames chascuns rebrachie
> Chelui qui soif avout ont la boche moillie;
> Chascun ont abevre; ce fu moult grans ale.
> Se les dames ne fussent, moult fust l'os mailbaillie.[148]

Again during the same conquest the women made themselves useful by carrying water to the wounded,[149] an important service on the battlefield.

In addition to healing wounds, women performed various other services, including the setting of broken arms and dislocated shoulders. Setting Kay's broken arm in *Perceval* seemed to call for professional aid,[150] although Aucassin's dislocated shoulder offered no great problem to Nicolette, who reduced it with her own hands,[151] and then applied a poultice of flowers and leaves. In actual practice Guy de Chauliac used a similar treatment, when he recommended pushing a dislocated shoulder into place with the palm of the hand covered with oil, and then applying, during the first painful days, a plaster made of wheat and red powder.[152]

146. Malory, *op. cit.*, Bk. I, Chaps. LXXI, XCV; Kristian von Troyes, *Der Karrenritter*, ll. 3497 ff., and *Der Percevalroman*, ed. Alfons Hilka (Halle, 1932), ll. 4330 ff.
147. Malory, *op. cit.*, Bk. VIII, Chap. VIII.
148. Le Pélerin Richard, *La Conquête de Jérusalem*, ed. C. Hippeau (Paris, 1868), ll. 3188 ff.
   To this place came the women each tucked up;
   He who was thirsty had his lips moistened;
   Each was given a drink; this was a very great help.
   If the women had not been there, the host would have been in a bad plight.
149. *Ibid.*, l. 469.
150. See *infra*, p. 99.
151. *Aucassin et Nicolette*, Sec. XXVI, ll. 10 ff.
152. Guy de Chauliac, *op. cit.*, pp. 377–78.

Although wounds acquired on the battlefield claimed the attention of most fictional women healers, some of these medical heroines ministered to patients suffering from some of the other complaints and ailments that engrossed the attention of physicians in town and city. The less there was known about a disease in scientific medicine, the greater was the likelihood of supernatural treatment of it in fiction. It was inevitable, therefore, that fantastic theories of the causes and cures of leprosy and insanity should gain currency among the physicians, and that the writers of romance should be willing to solve the difficulties through supernatural dispensation. The remedies for insanity in Bartholomew's *De proprietatibus rerum*[153] were a combination of magic and medicine, which represented actual practice at that time. When, therefore, Yvain roamed the forest, mad from grief at having forgotten to keep the tryst with a lady, the reader feels certain that in spite of his ailment he will be cured. He was discovered by two damsels and their mistress, the latter the possessor of a precious ointment, given her by Morgan the Wise, which could cure any delirium.[154] The mistress instructed one of the girls to rub the ointment only on Yvain's forehead. In her anxiety to heal the knight, the girl used the entire box and rubbed it not on his temples only but over his body as well. She was severely reprimanded by her mistress, who advised her that the box was her best and dearest possession.[155] Yvain was given a bath and a much-needed shave; every want was supplied, whether arms or a horse. Before long, strength and sanity returned. The mother of Amadas, in *Amadas et Ydoine*,[156] tried to relieve her son with several medicines after he had lost his mind upon hearing of Ydoine's marriage, but all were to no avail. Ydoine assured him of her love, and was thereby able to restore his sanity.[157] Dame Brisen, in the *Morte Darthur*,[158] resorted to enchantments to restore Lancelot's mind when he had lost it from lack of nourishment and the pain of a severe wound. The cures

---

153. Bartholomâeus Anglicus, *De proprietatibus rerum*. Cf. the translation by John of Trevisa (London, 1495), Lib. 7, cap. v.
154. Kristian von Troyes, *Der Löwenritter*, ed. Wendelin Foerster (Halle, 1887), ll. 2952 ff. Cf. Hartmann von Aue, *Iwein* (ed. by G. F. Benecke and K. Lachmann [Berlin, 1827], ll. 3423 ff., in which the salve is made by "Feimorgan." In *Ywain and Gawain* (ed. Gustav Schleich [Leipzig and Oppeln, 1887], ll. 1755 ff.), Morgan the Wise is referred to as a man:

> *He* sayd: This unement es so gode,
> That, if a man be braynwode
> And he war anes anoynt with yt,
> Smertly sold he have his wit.

155. Kristian von Troyes, *Der Löwenritter*, ll. 3124 ff.
156. *Amadas et Ydoine*, ed. C. Hippeau (Paris, 1868), ll. 1944 ff.
157. *Ibid.*, l. 3397.
158. Malory, *op. cit.*, Bk. XII, Chap. V.

in these various cases of insanity were obviously composed of more magic than medicine.

Few healers in fiction were called upon to treat cases of leprosy. Since the disease was so loathsome and the cure so improbable in actual experience, leprosy, like insanity, was ordinarily cured in fiction by means of magic or miracle. Several victims were healed by blood.[159] Women healers were as much at a loss as doctors to know how to deal with leprous patients. In the English version of *Amis and Amiloun*,[160] Belisaunt, the wife of Amis, gave Amiloun, who had become a leper, the wisest care she knew when she bathed him and gave him rich clothes. Most lepers followed the example of Cressida, in *The Testament of Cresseid*, who begged her father to send her to a leper hospital:

> "Thairfor in secreit wyse ye let me gang
> To yon hospitall at the tounis end;
> And thidder sum meit, for cheritie, me send
> To leif upon . . ."[161]

In the leper hospitals, although food was not plentiful, the lepers received better care than when they begged for a living as outcasts and "meseles in hegges."[162]

To put oneself in the hands of one of these amateur healers was doubtless to take risks. One still takes the risks of a wrong diagnosis and mistaken treatment when one consults the great professional specialists today. Evidently these medieval women had acquired a good deal of sound elementary knowledge as to the treatment of wounds and sores, based on experience. They knew the importance of rest and sleep, the efficacy of hot baths and herbal concoctions. Some of them at least could treat a dislocated shoulder or a broken bone. And most of them were not bothered by the erudite hocuspocus which was the stock-in-trade of their professional brethren.

159. See *Amis et Amiles und Jourdains de Blaivies*, ed. Konrad Hofmann (Erlangen, 1882), ll. 22,909 ff.; Hartmann von Aue, *Der Arme Heinrich*, ed. John G. Robertson (London, 1895); *Amis and Amiloun*, ed. MacEdward Leach, EETS, Vol. CCIII (1937), note, lxii; and John Gower, "Confessio Amantis," in *The English Works of John Gower*, ed. G. G. Macaulay, EETS, Vol. LXXXI–LXXXII (1901), Bk. II, ll. 3206 ff.
160. *Amis and Amiloun*, ll. 2179 ff.
161. Robert Henryson, "The Testament of Cresseid," *The Poems of Robert Henryson*, ed. W. M. Metcalfe (Paisley, 1917), ll. 381 ff.
162. *Piers the Plowman*, B text, l. 132.

Chapter Four

ACADEMIC MEDICINE

I N THE MIDDLE AGES, most of the healing work that fell to the lot of women was carried out by women who were self-taught, who relied on the knowledge they gained from contemporary usage, or who merely used their wits to deal with illnesses and accidents that confronted them in their homes; but the picture of medieval women in medicine would not be complete if the few who aspired to the same degree of "scientific" training as the university-trained medical men were not mentioned or if a brief survey of what was taught and practiced in academic medicine were omitted. These women had almost insuperable difficulties to contend with, and of those who persevered in spite of all obstacles that were placed in their way some won fame, and the names of one or two of them have been recorded. In the fourteenth century, Costanza Calenda of Naples won distinction as a lecturer in medicine, and Maestra Antonia of Florence, who lived between the years 1386 and 1408, was also the possessor of a medical degree. But the number of such women was strictly limited, since universities elsewhere in Europe refused to open their doors to women students. However, what went on within the walls of the inhospitable medical schools exerted an important influence on the methods and principles of men and women healers alike. Excluded from the classrooms, the women sought to learn "scientific" medicine from the more fortunate men students and to copy their techniques. Thus academic medicine to no small degree conditioned medical knowledge and usage throughout the ranks of the healers and became more and more distorted as it passed from the most enlightened practitioners to the most completely ignorant.

The conditions under which men and women learned and practiced medicine in the later Middle Ages were largely determined by the development of the universities. Before the organization of the universities, men and women learned a smattering of theory and treatment from experienced physicians, surgeons, and barber-surgeons, and then carried on their own practices with almost no restrictions upon their activities. The principal measuring stick employed by society was the practitioner's ability to effect a cure. Then came the medical school at Salerno, which functioned as early as the eleventh century. With the twelfth century, however, the rise of other universities began, and with them started a general revolution in medical training. The period became one of transition from the apprentice system in medicine to one of regular training of the young student at a medical school. In Italy by the thirteenth century a license from the corporation of physicians was required in most cities, even in many of those which did not have universities. By the sixteenth century, control of medical practice was concentrated in the hands of university and state authorities who prohibited from practice, with some degree of success, those who had not received a license to practice or university training in addition to a license to practice. This meant that most women were excluded from the profession, since, with few exceptions, the universities did not accept women students.

It was during the twelfth and thirteenth centuries also that medicine became exclusively a secular science, when various laws were imposed on the clergy prohibiting the shedding of blood. In 1163 the clergy in office were prohibited from practicing surgery by the Council of Tours under the direction of Alexander III.[1] Pope Honorius III (1216–27) extended this prohibition to the practice of medicine.[2] In 1215 the Fourth Lateran Council ordered subdeacons, deacons, and priests to abstain from the practice of surgery, especially when it involved burning or cutting.[3] Surgery was given over to the university-trained surgeons and to the barbers, who had for some time been assistants to monks who practiced surgery, and who now called themselves barber-surgeons.

In the transitional period, while the universities were gaining a tenuous hold over medicine and were experimenting with medical courses, the experiences of practitioners presented an interesting study of struggle between superstition and science, rivalry between universities, opposition to new ideas, and efforts to eliminate persons without academic training. A host of men and women who acquired enough training and skill to practice were unrecognized by academic or civic authority but became conscientious and often efficient practitioners. They constituted the better class of empirics. The fact that they had received no academic, formal instruction, directly or indirectly, distinguished them from the university-trained physicians, and led the physicians to denounce their work and to classify them all as charlatans. The modern definition of "empiric" suggests that the person may merit this classification, for the empiric is defined as (1) one who relies upon practical experience; and

1. *Sacrorum conciliorum nova et amplissima collectio*, ed. G. D. Mansi (Florence, 1759–98), Vol. XXI, col. 1160.
2. *Ibid.*, Vol. XXIII, col. 756.
3. *Ibid.*, Vol. XXII, col. 1010.

(2) a quack, or charlatan. But in the Middle Ages not all empirics were charlatans. Many received instruction from physicians trained in the medical schools, which together with their practical experience enabled them to compete successfully with the instructors themselves. Others doubtless had access to manuscripts containing academic lore, for manuscripts were copied frequently for students, physicians, and medical school libraries. Many empirics, on the other hand, were unable to read the Latin manuscripts. It was to the interests of medicine to raise the standards of the profession and to curb the practices of the empirics by directing young medical students to the universities. If women had been permitted to attend the universities in France and England, as they were some of those in Italy, they might have taken a more active part in the gradual raising of medical standards. As empirics, however, they had little opportunity to become well informed of medical theory or to improve their methods of healing.

The principal difference between the knowledge of the woman empiric and the physician trained at the university lay in the fund of philosophy, logic, and medical theory which the university student learned along with the exact application of this knowledge to medicine. Three years of logic were required of the physician in a decree of Frederick II, and at Bologna Aristotelian physiology was firmly allied with the study of medicine. Moreover, the university as the training ground for the physician became the source of both the discovery and the dissemination of important medical knowledge. The great physicians and surgeons of the period were university-trained men, and many of them taught at one or more of the medical schools. Empirics collected a wealth of remedies but lacked the physician's knowledge of how and when to administer them, and failed to keep abreast of the new medical practice. The situation was ironic, to be sure, in that some of the academic theories were not founded upon fact, and the practices of the physicians at the medical schools were at times less successful than those of the empiric. Yet the physician's knowledge, no less than that of the empiric, pointed the way to medical progress.

What the physician knew may be gathered from various contemporary sources. To begin with, the textbooks on the required reading lists of the medical schools furnished his general background in the field of medicine. In the next place, the treatises which he wrote indicated the scope of his knowledge and research. Again, these treatises sometimes set forth his own conception of professional medical men. And finally, the literary works of laymen sketched the physician's training and practice. Combining the information from these sources, we may offer a brief survey of the academic centers and the books which contributed to medical knowledge, and of the theories and practices of the licensed doctor of physic.

Of the universities which were important for medicine, Salerno was the first to achieve fame. Obscurity still surrounds the origin of the medical school, but at least by the eleventh century it was renowned for the skill of its physicians,[4] and, until its decline in the thirteenth century, it attracted students from East and West. Although it is not certain whether the school admitted women students, a number of women who engaged in medical work have been traditionally associated with Salerno. In the twelfth century Paris included a medical faculty in its *studium generale*, and Salerno's great rival, Montpellier, was established, although there is no reference to its medical school before the thirteenth century. Bologna, at first a school of law, founded its scientific school of medicine about 1260. The status of its medical doctors was inferior to that of its jurists until the fourteenth century, when its increased attention to surgery contributed to progress in that field. Oxford began to give medical instruction in the thirteenth century. In the following century men like John of Gaddesden, who took his medical degree there, brought credit and fame to the school. Medical schools were founded at Barcelona in 1401, at Caen in 1431, at Angers in 1432. The German universities, which were not created until the fourteenth and fifteenth centuries, contributed little at the time to medical science.

Many of the books studied at the medical schools were made available through the efforts of a number of men and one woman at Salerno. The *Antidotarium*, written by Nicholas in the eleventh century, contained from 140 to 150 somewhat complicated medical recipes. Quoted and studied continuously, these became the basis of the later pharmacopoeias. A compendium of popular cures, the *De modo medendi* (12 c.) also became widely known. The *Anatomia porci*, a handbook of the early twelfth century describing the dissection of a pig, was attributed to Copho and was said to be the earliest Salernitan book on anatomy. The *Practica chirurgiae*, edited by Roger (fl. 1170), became the leading textbook on surgery of the thirteenth century. Most popular of all the Salernitan works was the *Regimen sanitatis Salernitanum*, which was a composite of hygiene and medicine in 362 lines of Leonine verse. Written in the twelfth century, it became a sort of medical Bible for the later

---

4. Ordericus Vitalis in the twelfth century stated that the school had existed from ancient times. *Historia ecclesiastica* in "Patrologiae Latinae," ed. J. P. Migne, Vol. CLXXXVIII (Paris, 1855), col. 260. Cf. Hastings Rashdall, *The Universities of Europe in the Middle Ages*, ed. F. M. Powicke and A. B. Emden (Oxford, 1936), I, 75 ff.

Middle Ages, and not to have memorized its codes of health was a serious omission on the part of any physician. Arnold of Villanova (d. 1311) brought out a revised version of it, and in this way he helped to extend its popularity among educated laymen. The *De passionibus mulierum*, attributed to Trotula (11 c.), which will be discussed more fully in Chapter VI, remained one of the standard reference books on gynecology until the sixteenth century.

The Moslem works studied at the universities were introduced to Salerno and to the later schools principally through Latin translations. After their invasion of Persia, Egypt, and Syria, the Arabs were quick to borrow the Greek culture of the captive countries, and to make translations of the Greek medical treatises. Some of these in turn were translated into Latin by Constantinus Africanus in the eleventh century; many others, by Gerard of Cremona in the twelfth.

Several Moslems gained distinction and won respect from the medieval physicians for their translations of Greek medical works, their interpretations of Aristotelian philosophy, and for their own treatises. Al Razi (850–923), Chaucer's "Razis," a Persian by birth, described by Sarton as "the greatest clinician of Islam and of the whole Middle Ages,"[5] wrote the *Al-hawi*, or *Continens*, a vast enclyclopedia composed of extracts from numerous sources and accounts of his own clincial experience. Avicenna (Abu 'Ali Husayn Ibn Abdu 'llah Ibn Sina [980–1037]), another Persian, was physician-in-chief to the hospital at Bagdad and was called by his countrymen "the prince of physicians." He became famous for his *Canon*, in which he discussed, among other subjects, physiology, anatomy, surgery, midwifery, and materia medica, continuing the tradition of Aristotle in philosophy and of Galen in his interpretation of medical information. With him originated the practice of dressing wounds with wine and the notion that surgery was an inferior art in medical practice.[6] Avicenna's *Canon* was accepted as the standard textbook in medicine. The *Khihaab el Maleki*, or *The Royal Art of Medicine*, of Ali Ibn Abbas (d. 994), was a reference book for general medicine, which treated first the theory, then the practice of medicine. The last of the Moslems famous as writers of textbooks was Averroës (1126–98), philosopher and physician of Cordova, a man of considerable influence in state affairs as well as in medicine. His contribution to the history of medicine was the *Colliget*, a lengthy commentary on the *Canon* of Avicenna.

To their second-hand Greek culture the Moslems added a keen interest in alchemy and astrology, and a wealth of new medical botany. Among

5. George Sarton, *Introduction to the History of Science* (Baltimore, Md., 1927), I, 609.
6. *Ibid.*, I, 709–10.

other things, they made a careful study of Arabian trees and shrubs. In consequence, Arabia came to supply the world with aromatic gums and spices, such as cinnamon, myrrh, cassis, and olibanum. Drugs, such as senna, tamarind, musk, camphor, nutmeg, and cloves supplemented those used by the Greeks. Arabian laboratories were the first to produce distilled water and to make familiar such names as sirup, alkali, and naphtha.

These original contributions of the Moslems to later medicine were slight, however, in comparison with their service in reviving the influence of Greek medicine through their translations. The works of Hippocrates and Galen, in particular, were studied and used as the basis for most of the Moslem medical treatises. Galen, for example, was translated into Arabic by Hunain ben Isaac (Abu Zaid Hunain ibn Ishap al-'Ibadi—in Latin, Joannitius—[809?-77]) and was the basis for *The Royal Art of Medicine* of Ali Ibn Abbas. Constantinus Africanus then translated *The Royal Art of Medicine* into Latin about 1080. The work was later improved upon by Stephen of Pisa at Antioch. The works of Isaac Israeli (d. 932?), dealing with fevers, were based on Arabic sources. These translations perpetuated Hippocratic and Galenic theories with the result that later medieval medicine was thoroughly saturated with them, and one had only to call a remedy "Hippocratic" or "Galenic" to give it the greatest prestige.

The works of Hippocrates, Aristotle, and Galen were known before the Moslems added their influence to the revival of Greek culture, and many of the Greek works were translated directly from the Greek. Manuscript copies were available outside the universities as well as for academic use. Hippocrates (b. 460 B.C.), who deserved his place in the affections of the medieval doctors, was the first to establish medicine upon a rational basis and to introduce inductive medicine. He composed aphorisms for the cure of disease, recommended diet and exercise, and initiated clinical medicine. So carefully were the records of his cases kept that modern physicians have pointed to them as models. The Hippocratic *Corpus*, which has come down to us, is the work, not only of Hippocrates, but also of his school.

The Hippocratic theory of the four humors, with which Pertelote was familiar in the fourteenth century, was rarely questioned by either doctor or layman. Hippocrates believed that the body of man contained blood, phlegm, yellow bile, and black bile, which determined man's nature and his health.[7] These humors, he thought, had their seats in the four parts

7. Hippocrates, "The Nature of Man," in *Hippocrates*, translated W. H. S. Jones (London, 1931), IV, 11. And see *The Genuine Works of Hippocrates*, tr. from the Greek by Francis Adams (New York, 1891), pp. 85-87.

of the body: blood, in the arteries and veins; phlegm, in the brain; yellow bile, in the liver; and black bile, in the spleen. The humors acted in different ways upon the body, blood making the spirit wilder; yellow bile making it bolder; black bile, firmer; and phlegm, sluggish. An insufficiency or an overabundance of one or more of the humors produced illness.

To the theory of humors Aristotle (384–322 B.C.) added his own theory of the qualities, heat, cold, moistness, dryness. He thought that all matter, including man's body, was, to a degree, hot or cold, moist or dry. From both Hippocrates and Aristotle, Galen (b. 130 A.D.), the famous Greek medical philosopher, ingenious theorist, and facile writer, borrowed freely. He combined the Aristotelian theory of the four qualities with the four elements, earth, air, fire, and water, and thus produced the theory of the "complexions," or temperaments, of men. Men were accordingly sanguine, phlegmatic, melancholic, or choleric. The sanguine man was hot and moist, like the air; the phlegmatic man was cold and moist, like the water; the melancholic man was cold and dry, like the earth; and the choleric man was hot and dry, like fire.

The collected works of Galen represented the medical knowledge of his day, and included books on anatomy, physiology, pathology, the pulse, therapeutics, practice, and pharmacy.[8] Until the seventeenth century, when most of his work was proved to be incorrect, paraphrases and new editions of his work were constantly appearing. Herbs and drugs composed a major part of his medicine, and Galen emphasized the importance of a knowledge of them and of personal experience in compounding and administering them.

Although he ridiculed the simples and practices of many doctors, and considered charms, incantations, and philters as dangerous and ineffectual, Galen prescribed medicines whose ingredients were not unrelated to those of witches' cauldrons. He used the bile of bulls, cocks, and hyenas;[9] a digestive oil made by cooking foxes and hyenas, some alive and some dead;[10] and medicines containing a spider's web, a sheepskin, and the sloughed skin of a snake.[11] With all his ingenuity and his scientific attitude, he could not escape the superstitions of his age.

For the students at the medical schools Hunain ben Isaac (809–77)

8. The Greek text and Latin translation of Galen's works were edited by D. Carolus Gottlob Kühn in twenty volumes in *Claudii Galeni opera omnia* (Leipzig, 1821–23).
9. Galen, "De simplicium medicamentorum tempera mentis ac jocultatibus," in *Claudii Galeni opera omnia*, XII, 276–77. See Lynn Thorndike, *History of Magic and Experimental Science* (New York, 1923), I, 168.
10. Galen, *op. cit.*, XII, 367, 369. See Thorndike, *loc. cit.*
11. Galen, *op. cit.*, XII, 343. See Thorndike, *loc. cit.*

offered in *The Isagogue*,[12] his introduction to Galen's *Ars parva*, a convenient summary of the master's teaching. This work became extremely popular as a guide in the later centuries. Hunain asserted that the two parts of medicine were the theoretic and the practical. The theoretic was divided into three further parts: the naturals, the nonnaturals, and the contranaturals. From consideration of these arose knowledge of sickness, health, and the mean state. There were seven naturals: elements, qualities, humors, numbers, energies, operations, and spirits, to which some added age, color, figure, and the distinction between male and female. There were four elements—earth, air, fire, and water—and nine qualities—the simple ones, hot, cold, moist, and dry, and their compounds. The state of health indicated that the body was in good condition and in a mean state, and that it had the proper amount of all four humors. There were five varieties of phlegm, two different types of reddish bile, and two of black bile. There were four kinds of members, some principal, and some which served the principals. The three energies were animal, spiritual, and natural, each of which served the others and was served by still others. There were three spirits: the natural spirit, having its origin in the liver; the vital spirit, in the heart; and the animal spirit, in the brain. Man passed through four ages: adolescence, prime, decline, and decay, each of which was characterized by particular qualities. Colors of the skin and hair belonged to general types. The five qualities of the body explained all deviations from the normal, such as excess in flesh, which arose from excess of heat and humors, and loss of fat, which came from heat and intense dryness. Differences between the male and the female accounted for some of their characteristics: the male was hotter and more dry; the female was cooler and more moist.

Discussion of the nonnaturals included consideration of subjects such as changes of air, the seasons, the winds, places, baths, food, drink, sleep, and the mind. Each season was characterized by qualities, spring, for example, being hot and moist. The winds had numbers and properties. Baths produced special effects upon the body; for fresh-water baths softened it, and those in salt or sulphurous waters dried and heated it. Some food brought on good humors, and others, evil humors. For example, nasturtium, mustard, and garlic produced reddish bile; lentils, cabbage, and the meat of old goats and beeves begot black bile. Heavy foods produced phlegm and black bile; light foods, reddish bile; but both forms of bile were evil. There were three kinds of drink: pure drink, like water; a combination of food and drink, like wine; and a drink that in-

12. H. P. Cholmeley, *John of Gaddesden and the Rosa Medicinae* (Oxford, 1912), Appendix D.

cluded both of these, called *potio*, given to counteract the evil of a disease.
The condition of the mind reacted upon the body, as in the case of anger,
delight, or joy.

The nonnaturals involved disease, the cause of disease, and their
concomitants. There were the three kinds of fever: ephemeral fever,
which arose in the spirit; putrid fever, which arose from the humors; and
hectic fever, which affected all the solid portions of the body. Four
special types of fever affected man. The first, continued fever or *sinochus*,
arose from putridity of the blood and burned up both the interior and the
exterior of the body. The second, tertian fever, arose from putridity of
reddish bile. The third, quotidian fever, arose from putridity of phlegm.
The fourth, quartan fever, came from putridity of black bile and attacked
the sick man after an interval of two days. Swellings were also divided
into four classes, according to their origin. Diseases were known as
similar, official, and universal. Those in similar members arose from the
qualities or compounds of them. Those in the official members were
classified according to shape, size, number, and position. The causes of
sickness were either natural or outside the course of nature. There were
five ways in which disease might arise from heat, eight ways from cold,
four ways from dryness, and four ways from moisture.

Since the practice of medicine, as Hunain stated, dealt with the right
ordering of nonnaturals, with giving of drugs (*potio*), and with surgery,
the female empiric could not treat a patient in the same way as the
physician would. She could neither diagnose the case, nor could she
decide by "scientific" calculation whether to administer the drugs internally by the mouth, the ears, the nose, or other aperture; or externally,
by poultices, plasters, or stupes, as the physicians were taught to do.
When it came to knowing herbs, the empirics displayed as much practical
knowledge as the doctors, but they could not compete with the medical
man's information concerning drugs, their quality and quantity, the
best seasons for their use, and the question of whether they were good or
bad.

The textbooks on the reading lists of the medical schools stressed the
importance of theoretical knowledge, and they demonstrated the increasing respect with which the later Middle Ages regarded the Moslem medical works. In 1309 Clement V, on the advice of Montpellier physicians,
decreed that the candidates for the license at the University of Montpellier should possess the following books: Galen's *De complexionibus*,
De malicia complexionis diverse, *De simplici medicina*, *De morbo et accidente*, *De crisi et criticis diebus*, *De ingenio sanitatis*, together with either

the books of Avicenna or those of Roger, Constantinus Africanus, and Isaac, with commentaries on them.[13]

Candidates must also have read as bachelors three books, two with and one without comments, selected from the following:

The *Tegni* of Galen
The *Prognostica* and *Aphorismi* of Hippocrates
The *De regimine acutorum* of Joannitius
The *Liber febribus* of Isaac
The *Antidotarium* of Nicholas
The *De morbo et accidente* of Galen
The *De ingenio sanitatis* of Galen[14]

In 1340 the following books were set as subjects for lectures, given in courses and required of each candidate at Montpellier:

The *Primus canonis* of Avicenna
The *Liber de morbe et accidente* and *Differentiis febrium* of Galen
The *Liber de crisi et criticis diebus* and *De malicia complexionis diverse*
The *Liber de simplicibus medicinis* and *De complexionibus*
The *Liber de iuvamentis membrorum* and *De interioribus*
Hippocrates' *Liber aphorismorum* with his *De regimine acutorum* or his *De prognosticis*
The *Liber de ingenio* (sanitatis) and *Ad Glauconem* of Galen
The *Quartus canonis* of Avicenna
Galen's *Tegni* with the *De prognosticis* and *De regimine acutorum* of Hippocrates
Liber de regimine sanitatis and Bartholomew's *De virtutibus naturalibus*[15]

If there were enough doctors to lecture, there might be additional lectures on other parts of the canon, other books of Galen, or the *De febribus* and *De dietis universalibus* of Isaac.

A wealth of other medical and philosophical treatises was available to medical students by the fourteenth century. To the commentaries on the Greek works were added commentaries on the Moslem texts, and prolific and influential writers like Arnold of Villanova, Peter of Abano, and

13. *Cartulaire de l'université de Montpellier*, published under the auspices of the Conseil général des Facultés de Montpellier (Montpellier, 1890), I, 220. Cf. Rashdall, *op. cit.*, II, 127.
14. *Cartulaire*, I, 220.   15. *Ibid.*, I, 347, 348.

Taddeo Alderotti contributed numerous works of importance to medicine and philosophy.

Toward the end of the thirteenth century physicians and surgeons in many European countries formed two separate groups of healers. From that time on, physicians concerned themselves with internal maladies and looked down upon the surgeons who attended especially to external troubles and performed major operations. Men who wished to specialize in surgery studied surgical texts with a surgeon connected with a university. Considerable jealousy arose between physicians and surgeons because of this division of their work. Italy presented an exception to the general practice, for there surgery was taught by doctors of medicine who engaged in surgical practice and did not consider the manual work of the surgeon as degrading craft.

Surgery, too, had its classics, of which one of the earliest following the Salernitan works was the *Cyrurgia* (1275) of the great Italian, Guglielmo Saliceto. The work was translated into English, Italian, Bohemian, French, and Hebrew. Saliceto was one of the first to break away from traditional practice. He condemned the traditional use of the cautery and recommended that of the scalpel. He kept a record of his case histories; he showed how to diagnose bleeding from an artery by a spurt of blood; he described melancholia satisfactorily; and he was the first to record a group of symptoms now associated with Bright's disease.[16]

Saliceto's pupil, Lanfranc of Milan (fl. 1290), was banished from his home because of the Guelph-Ghibelline quarrel, and settled in Paris, where he lectured at the College de St. Come and became the "virtual founder of French surgery."[17] His principal works were the *Chirurgia parva* and the *Chirurgia magna*. He insisted upon general knowledge of medicine and clinical study for surgeons. Outstanding among his contributions to surgery were his descriptions of concussion of the brain and fracture of the skull, of reaction to excessive trepanation, and of treatment in the case of hernia. The *Chirurgia magna* was translated into English in 1300, and it is important because it was the earliest surgical and anatomical work in that language.

As far as general healing was concerned, Lanfranc followed current practices. He continued Galen's theory of curing by opposites and recommended that a patient of hot and moist complexion in fever resulting from a wound should be given such treatments as bloodletting on the opposite side of the wound, cupping, purging, sewing up the wound, or the use of bandages, the application of a "defensive medicine" made of

16. Sarton, *op. cit.*, II, 1079–81.   17. *Ibid.*, II, 1079.

oil of roses and vinegar, and a diet excluding wine, milk, iron, and fish, but containing oatmeal gruel.[18] He prescribed for an open wound a medicament made of wheat flour, honey, water, rosewater, and barley meal.[19] To repair the flesh when part of the bone was removed or refastened, he recommended a powder made of frankincense, mastic myrrh, Arabic gum, dragon seed, and flower of fenugreek.[20] If the case were a wound, the patient was always to be bled.[21]

Lanfranc summarized the medieval beliefs in regard to bloodletting,[22] the practice which doctors had inherited from classical medicine and grimly pursued until the nineteenth century, when the operation was finally dropped from general treatment. Lanfranc stated that bloodletting was used to keep a man's body cool and to relieve it of sickness. The attending physician should keep in mind the hour, the time, the air, and the disposition of the sick man. No man should suffer bloodletting unless he could endure it. It was thought to be good principally for those who ate and drank much and exercised little, for the prevention of disease, for the cooling of passion: in short, for all those whose illnesses were caused by too much blood. An operator should be young, have good sight, know veins and arteries, and have various tools, all of which should be clean.

Lanfranc, like other scientific doctors, included in his medicine the most unscientific remedies. When he discussed leprosy, he stated that the patient should be given good meat and drink, not too hot and not too cold. He then repeated a cure which was often quoted as a treatment for leprosy, and which, according to him, other doctors used.[23] The patient was given a broth made of the flesh of a black snake caught in a dry land among stones. The flesh was cooked in an earthen vessel with a little pepper, galyngale,[24] salt, vinegar, water, and oil. This broth would make the patient dizzy and cause his body to swell, whereupon he should be given theriac major and a little hot wine. His flesh would then peel, his hair fall away, and new hair would come. The medicine was to be repeated often. In spite of such remedies, Lanfranc maintained a high standard in practice and condemned the "wretched leech" who for per-

18. Lanfranc, *Science of Cirurgie*, ed. Robert v. Fleischhacker, EETS, Vol. CII (1894), 12–13.
19. *Ibid.*, p. 49.
20. *Ibid.*
21. *Ibid.*
22. *Ibid.*, pp. 298–305.
23. *Ibid.*, p. 198.
24. A popular flavor prepared from sweet cyperus, salt, vinegar, water, and oil. The name of the herb, galangal, was often spelled in the same way.

sonal gain or other reasons would endanger a man's life by administering the wrong treatment.[25]

Credit for the revival of the practice of dissecting human bodies goes to Mundinus (or Mondino) de Luzzi, who taught at the University of Bologna and who in 1313 dissected two female bodies for the instruction of his students. Dissections of cadavers had been made during the previous two centuries, but were so rare that the general knowledge of anatomy on the part of teachers or students in medical schools was negligible. In the fourteenth century dissections were finally permitted at Bologna, Venice, and Montpellier. The time had not yet come for the anatomist to dissect a body and lecture upon what he saw. Mundinus wrote the *Anatomia corporis humanis* (1316), manuscripts of which were sometimes illustrated with a picture of an anatomist sitting upon a platform while an assistant performed a dissection, the anatomist reading from Galen the very statements which the dissections should have disproved. The cadavers studied by Mundinus evidently did not add to, or detract from, the ideas of Hippocrates, Galen, Ali Ibn Abbas, and others who were quoted in the *Anatomia*. This work was the accepted textbook in medieval schools for more than a century, passing through thirty-nine separate editions and translations. One of Mundinus's assistants was Alessandra Giliani, a young woman whom Mundinus had trained first in philosophy, then in anatomy. She had become so expert in dissection that she was made prosector, and was thus responsible for preparing the cadavers for demonstration.[26]

A higher standard in the practice in surgery was brought about through the influence of the medical schools in Italy and France and through royal decree. In 1240 Frederick II gave Salerno rules for the study of medicine there and, in doing so, supplied a standard for the European schools.[27] Montpellier, in 1239, passed the requirement that no student should practice independently without examination and approval by the bishop and his examiners.[28] As early as 1220 the University of Paris prohibited all from practicing medicine save those on its faculty, to which

25. Lanfranc, *op. cit.*, pp. 271–72.
26. See *infra*, pp. 86-7.
27. Frederick II himself astonished the Arabs with his knowledge of medicine and anatomy. See Ernst Kantorowicz, *Kaiser Friedrich der Zweite* (Berlin, 1931), p. 329. Frederick's decree read as follows: ". . . nisi Salerni primitus in conventu publico magistrorum iudicio comprobatus, cum testimonialibus literis de fide et sufficienti scientia tam magistrorum quam ordinatorum nostrorum, ad presentiam nostram vel, nobis a regno absentibus, ad illius presentiam qui vice nostra in regno remanserit [ordinatus accedat] et a nobis vel ab eo medendi licentiam consequatur." *Historia diplomatica Friderici Secundi*, ed. J. L. A. Huillard-Bréholles (Paris, 1850), IV, pt. 1, 150.
28. *Cartulaire*, I, 202.

only bachelors could be admitted,[29] thus attempting to sound the death knell to the ambitions of men and women who under other circumstances might have risen above the ranks of minor practitioners. A century later, in 1311, surgeons who wished to practice in Paris were required to pass an examination before the master of surgeons.[30]

Three great surgeons, Henri de Mondville, John Arderne, and Guy de Chauliac, practiced in the later Middle Ages and gained fame through their original contributions to medicine. Henri de Mondville (1260–1320), first a military surgeon, then surgeon to Philip the Fair, endeavored to bring surgery in France to the honored position which it already held in Italy. Following his progressive predecessors, he taught that wounds should heal without suppuration, and that they should be washed only with wine.

John Arderne (1307–80?), though trained abroad, practiced for many years in Nottinghamshire and became the best English surgeon of his century. One of the few surgeons and physicians to record failures as well as successes, Arderne also stressed the importance of personal experience in surgery.[31] Among medical historians he achieved fame for his practical treatment of fistula and diseases of the eye, and for his use of clysters and bleeding. The chapter on the fistula in his *Practica* was accepted by his contemporaries as an authoritative treatment of the condition. Like all doctors of his day, he relied principally upon herbal medicines for cures. Ingenious in preparing his prescriptions, he often gave them elaborate names, since he thought that by doing so he could protect them from use by laymen and unintelligent physicians.[32]

The pre-eminent figure in surgery in the fourteenth century was Guy de Chauliac (1300–68), "chirurgien et Maistre en médecine des frontières d'Auvergne, Diocèse de Mende, médecin et Chapelain commensal de nostre Seigneur le Pape."[33] Every advantage in medical training was his. He studied at Toulouse, Montpellier, Bologna, and Paris; he was physician to Popes Clement VI, Innocent VI, and Urban V. His *Chirugie* (1363) was the most scientific and clearly written book on surgery in the later Middle Ages. Compared to other medical books, it was free from superstitious and magical practices.

29. Jacoba Felicie referred to this law during her trial in 1322. *Auctarium chartularii universitatis parisiensis*, ed. Henricus Denifle, Aemilius Chatelain, *et al.* (Paris, 1937), II, 263. And see *infra*, p. 91. The law was not relaxed until 1452 under the influence of Cardinal Estouteville. See Rashdall, *op. cit.*, I, 446.
30. *Chart. Paris*, II, 434, 692.
31. John Arderne, *Treatises of Fistula in Ano*, ed. Sir D'Arcy Power, EETS, Vol. CXXXIX (1910), Preface.
32. *Ibid.*, p. 104.
33. Guy de Chauliac, *La Grande Chirurgie*, ed. E. Nicaise (Paris, 1910), p. 15.

De Chauliac's classification of the sects practicing surgery gives a reasonably clear idea of the types of operators in his day.[34] The first sect, he stated, used poultices and induced suppuration, treating all wounds and abscesses alike. The second group dried all wounds with a single wine on the theory that dryness approaches health, and moistness, illness. The third followed Guglielmo de Saliceto and Lanfranc, who clung to the middle of the road, and who treated all wounds with unguents and mild plasters. They based their practice upon the theory of a single, painless treatment. The fourth sect was composed of military men, Teutonic knights, and others following the army, who dressed all wounds with conjurations and potions, oil, woolens, and cabbage leaves, in the belief that God had given special virtues to words, herbs, and stones. The last sect, he declared, was composed of "women and many fools" who referred the sufferers of all illnesses to the saints alone, basing their practice upon the belief that the Lord had given as He had pleased, and the Lord would take away as He pleased. By casting all women healers into the fifth sect, de Chauliac chose to ignore the fact that many of them followed the practices of the first four groups.

Chaucer's Doctor of Physic was acquainted with the works of two Englishmen, Bernard Gordon and John of Gaddesden, who deserve mention, not for their scientific theories and practices, but rather for their reliance upon popular medicine. They represent the typical physician of the later Middle Ages. Bernard Gordon (fl. 1285–1318) was one of the early professors at Montpellier. He has been called "the Divine" because of his *Lilium medicinae*, a dogmatic medical treatise which he wrote in 1305, usually credited with being the first of a long line of books with flowery names. John of Gaddesden followed Bernard's example and named his medical book the *Rosa Anglica*. He seems to have been the first great English doctor educated solely in England. At Oxford he became Master of Arts, Bachelor of Theology, and Doctor of Medicine. He was appointed physician to Edward II. The *Rosa Anglica* was chiefly a repository of folk and Arabic superstitions, and no doubt it reflected the general state of medical training in England in the fourteenth century. Even his contemporary, Guy de Chauliac, condemned the book, saying, "J'avais creu de trouver en elle le suavité d'odeur. J'ay trouvé les fables de l'Espagnol, de Gilbert et Theodoric."[35]

Gaddesden's cures resembled those of earlier medieval medicine.[36]

---

34. *Ibid.*, pp. 15–16.
35. *Ibid.*, pp. 14–15.
36. No one was impervious to the superstitious ideas which characterized the age and appealed to all men. For some of the most popular superstitions in medical practice see Thomas Joseph Pettigrew, *On Superstitions Connected with the History and Practice of Medicine and Surgery* (Philadelphia, 1844).

Fever, he thought, was caused by hot foods; one should therefore give the patient food that would cool the stomach inside as well as outside.[37] He repeated the old superstitious belief that the roots of ragweed in wine would prevent fatigue produced by walking.[38] He agreed with Galen that water was not good for the young, since it was not nourishing; nor good for the old, since it was similar to their complexion.[39] With the same enthusiasm with which he prescribed remedies based upon classical or herbal medicine, he suggested a number of charms for toothache, for epilepsy, fevers, epistaxis, and scrofulous glands. If the patient suffered from toothache, the practitioner could prepare an amulet of the roots of *piloselle* (mouse-ear hawkweed) and *diptami* (dittany) to be worn around the neck, or he could select the most appropriate of the following charms and prayers:

1. Again, write these words on the jaw of the patient: In the name of the Father, the Son and the Holy Ghost, Amen.—*Rex—Pax—Nax—in Christo Filio*, and the pain will cease at once as I have often seen.

2. Again, whosoever shall say a prayer in honour of St. Apollonia, Virgin, (Feb. 9) shall have no pain in his teeth on the day of the prayer. The same thing is said of St. Nicasius the martyr (Oct. 11).

3. Again, draw characters on parchment or panel and let the patient touch the aching tooth with his finger as long as he is drawing, and he is cured. The characters are made in the shape of running water by drawing a continuous line, not straight but up and down. Three lines are to be drawn in the name of the Blessed Trinity and this is to be done often.

4. Again, if the many-footed "worm" which rolls up into a ball when you touch it is pricked with a needle and the aching tooth is then touched with the needle, the pain will be eased.

5. Again, some say that the beak of a magpie hung from the neck cures pain in the teeth and the uvula and the quinsy.

6. Again, when the gospel for Sunday is read in the mass, let the man hearing mass sign his tooth and his head with the sign of the cross and say a pater noster and an ave for the souls of the father and mother of St. Philip, and this without stopping; it will keep them from pain in the future and will cure that which may be present, so say trustworthy authorities.[40]

37. John of Gaddesden, *Rosa Anglica seu Rosa medicinae Johannis Anglici*, ed. Winifred Wulff, Irish Texts Society, Vol. XXV (<1923> 1929), 9, 11.
38. *Ibid.*, p. 63.
39. *Ibid.*, pp. 65, 67.
40. Cholmeley, *op. cit.*, pp. 48–52.

Gaddesden maintained a large practice and established a good reputation among English physicians and laymen alike. He was one of the doctors who between 1334 and 1335 visited the sick at Abingdon Abbey.[41] His appointment as royal physician indicated the favor which he enjoyed with the court of Edward II. Even today the *Rosa Anglica*, in spite of its antiquated medicine, is commended by medical historians for some of its clinical records.[42]

Astrology was accepted by medieval science in general, and belief in the influence of outside forces upon man's health, and especially that of the stars, affected academic medicine. Like all other sciences it called for skill and knowledge in its proper application. Physicians in the fourteenth and fifteenth centuries learned the celestial power influencing each of the twenty-four hours in order to diagnose a case and prescribe the correct treatment. They calculated the difference between the factors that operated at the patient's birth and those present at the time of his illness, and then they were in a position to prescribe the medicines which would restore the patient to a perfect balance of humors and qualities, and consequently to health. Gaddesden scarcely mentioned astrology in his book; yet John of Burgundy, in his *De pestilentia*, declared that physicians should possess knowledge of it when they treated victims of the plague.[43] Lanfranc had advised that bloodletting should be performed with the hour and the time in mind,[44] and Arderne thought it unwise to operate upon particular parts of the body while the moon was in Scorpion, Libra, or Sagittarius.[45] The learned Guy de Chauliac believed in astrology and attributed the black death to the disposition of the three superior bodies, Saturn, Jupiter, and Mars.[46]

People outside the medical profession watched with profound interest whatever was done to advance or retard medical practice. When there were abuses to be condemned, the layman raised his voice loudly in disapproval or subtly satirized them, and when there was evidence of professional excellence, the layman's voice was the first to praise it. Petrarch advised Boccaccio that the best way to keep well was to avoid calling in doctors.[47] Caxton, on the other hand, described the more conventional

41. *Accounts of the Obedientars of Abingdon Abbey*, ed. R. E. G. Kirk, Camden Society, LI (1892), 4–5.
42. See Cholmeley, *op. cit.*, p. 71, and Joseph Collins, "Medicine in England in Chaucer's Time," *Proceedings of the Charaka Club*, IV (New York, 1916), 145.
43. Cholmeley, *loc. cit.*
44. See *supra*, p. 73.
45. Arderne, *op. cit.*, pp. 16–17.
46. Guy de Chauliac, *op. cit.*, p. 171.
47. Francis Petrarch, "Epistolarum de rebus senilibus," *Francisci Petrarchae Florentine, philosophi . . . opera quae extant omnia* (Basle, 1581), Sec. V, iv.

understanding of the abilities and practices of the surgeon and the physician:

> Morysse the surgyan
> Medleth hym to hele
> Woundes, soores,
> And apostomes,
> With oynementis
> And with plastres;
> He can cutte out the stone,
> And hele by drynkes
> Of the grauelle and of brekynge.
>
> Maximian the maistre of phisike
> Seeth the vrin of the peple;
> He can seye to them
> Wherof they be seke;
> Of the heed ache;
> Of the payne of the eyen,
> Of the eres;
> Yf they haue toth ache;
> Atte the breste, at the pappes;
> He can hele and cure
> Dropesye, blody flyxe,
> Testyke, mormale,
> Feet nayles,
> Fever quartayn and tercian,
> Of the Jaundyse
> (Wherof god kepe vs),
> And of all that
> That may greue us.
> He gyueth conseill for the goute
> And for othir seknesses:
> He hath many good herbes.[48]

The descriptions of Morris and Maximian were brief copy-book examples of the medieval physician and surgeon. But the Doctor of Physic in the *Canterbury Tales* was a completely satisfactory representative of the medieval practitioner as he was seen by the great master of satire. The doctor was so steeped in theory which he had learned at the university

48. William Caxton, *Dialogues in French and English*, ed. Henry Bradley, EETS, Vol. LXXIX (1900), 41–42.

that, at least in his own opinion, he could scarcely fail in the application of his medicines.

> . . . ther was a Doctour of Phisik;
> In al this world ne was ther noon hym lik,
> To speke of phisik and of surgerye,
> For he was grounded in astronomye.
> He kepte his pacient a ful greet deel
> In houres by his magyk natureel.
> Wel koude he fortunen the ascendent
> Of hys ymages for his pacient.
> He knew the cause of everich maladye,
> Were it of hoot, or coold, or moyste, or drye,
> And where they engendred, and of what humour.
> He was a verray, parfit praktisour:
> The cause yknowe, and of his harm the roote,
> Anon he yaf the sike man his boote.
> Ful redy hadde he his apothecaries
> To sende hym drogges and his letuaries,
> For ech of hem made oother for to wynne—
> Hir frendshipe nas nat newe to bigynne.
> Wel knew he the olde Esculapius,
> And Deyscorides, and eek Rufus,
> Olde Ypocras, Haly, and Galyen,
> Serapion, Razis, and Avycen,
> Averrois, Damascien, and Constantyn,
> Bernard, and Gatesden, and Gilbertyn.
> Of his diete mesurable was he,
> For it was of no superfluitee,
> But of greet norissyng and digestible . . .[49]

His authorities, with the exception of the mythological Esculapius, were approved by all the medical writers. His confidence in his knowledge, his pseudo-scientific patter, and his lucrative practice would win the respect of all but the most perspicacious laymen. But Geoffrey Chaucer, who had a keen interest in frauds, broadly hints that here was a pretentious charlatan.

Some of the ablest medieval scientists belonged to the medical profession. Guy de Chauliac, for example, was one of these, and he was greatly

49. Geoffrey Chaucer, "Prologue to the Canterbury Tales," in *Works*, ed. F. N. Robinson (Cambridge, Mass., 1933), ll. 411 ff.

interested in maintaining high standards within the profession. But among the rank and file of medical men there was a marked tendency to fall back upon traditional lore and to encroach upon the domain of the much-condemned lay healer. When such inclinations led to flagrant abuses, the doctors themselves were the first to see what could be done to raise the standards of scientific medicine.

Chapter Five

WOMEN PRACTITIONERS

IN HISTORY

THE FORTUNES of the professional women healers in the late Middle Ages did not improve with the development of the universities. Before the founding of the medical schools, and in all countries except Italy, after the establishment of the schools, women received training either from experienced physicians, from empirics, or from charlatans. After the organization of the university medical schools, all the odds appeared to be against professional women. They were barred from attendance at all but the Italian universities, and this fact meant that they had to rely, for whatever they learned of the old and new medical theory and practice taught at the schools, upon any physicians who were willing to teach them. Under the circumstances, they had practically no opportunity of learning—even at secondhand—the logic, philosophy, and medical theory in which the university students' minds were steeped. However, for some time after the opening of the medical schools, new scientific methods did not noticeably affect the curricula. Herbal medicine, upon which earlier generations of healers had relied, continued to be taught. In addition, the cities and universities of the thirteenth and fourteenth centuries found it no easy matter to enforce the strict regulations they imposed upon those who wished to study and practice medicine. As a result, women managed to pursue their accustomed activities in all branches of medicine in spite of prohibitive legislation, although the changing conditions were responsible for the fact that women practitioners who were called "physicians" and "surgeons" flourished in greater numbers in the thirteenth century, whereas those whose practice caused them to be called "charlatans" were more prominent in the fourteenth and fifteenth centuries.

Civil restrictions placed upon the practice of medicine by women in the various European countries were closely linked to the educational facilities that were open to women students. Wherever the universities were closed to women, laws tended to be more strictly enforced, and punishment was meted out more severely to practicing physicians and surgeons who had not attended the medical schools. Italy offered women the most satisfactory conditions for both study and practice. The medical school at Salerno was apparently favorably disposed toward women in medicine, for at least one woman, Francesca, wife of Matteo de Romana, received a public certificate from the University of Salerno, stating that she possessed knowledge of surgery and had passed an examination before a commission of doctors and surgeons.[1] Moreover, several Italian women at Salerno were said to be authors of medical treatises.[2] One of these was Trotula, reputed to be the author of the important treatise on gynecology discussed in Chapter VI.

Women were also permitted to practice medicine and surgery in Florence, Venice, Naples, and Rome in the fourteenth and fifteenth centuries.[3] One fourteenth-century license granted to women opened with the statement: "Since, then, the law permitted women to exercise the profession of physicians and since, besides, due regard being had to purity of morals, women are better suited for the treatment of women's diseases, after having received the oath of fidelity, we permit. . ."[4] Further evidence that women were practicing medicine in Florence in the fifteenth century is found in the decree in which Pope Sixtus IV (1471–84) upheld an ordinance of the College of Physicians of Rome which stated that no man or woman, Christian or Jew, could subject the human body to medical or surgical treatment without license.[5]

Women were engaged in medical practice in France, but they encountered difficulties in the capital city when in the year 1220 the Faculty of Medicine of the University of Paris, which had established no uncertain control over the medical profession within its jurisdiction, prohibited all persons except the bachelors among the faculty members from the practice of medicine.[6] This ruling was so unreasonable that neither men nor women obeyed it for long. When the Paris census was taken in 1292, eight women physicians (*miresses*) were registered.[7] In 1311 a regulation came into force that required those who desired to practice medicine in Paris to be examined, before engaging in their profession, by a regularly appointed master of surgery.[8] Men and women continued to engage in medicine without license, occasionally having to pay a fine or be excommunicated for disregarding the law. A particularly thorough in-

1. Mélanie Lipinska, *Histoire des femmes médecins* (Paris, 1900), p. 99.
2. See Appendix I.
3. Lipinska, *op. cit.*, pp. 148–49.
4. J. J. Walsh, *Medieval Medicine* (London, 1930), p. 158.
5. Lipinska, *op. cit.*, p. 149.
6. See *supra*, pp. 74–75.
7. Hercule Géraud, *Paris sous Philippe de Bel d'après des documents originaux contenant le rôle de la taille* (Paris, 1837), pp. 57, 61, 65, 108, 134, 173, 179. See also *infra*, p. 141.
8. See *supra*, p. 75.

vestigation of practitioners was conducted in 1322, after which twenty-two men and three women were arraigned in the Paris courts.[9] The school of medicine at Montpellier passed laws similar to those of the University of Paris.[10]

There were no general regulations for the practice of medicine in medieval Germany, although in individual cities, as in Nuremberg, rules for such practice were passed in the fourteenth century. Under such conditions, men and women empirics flourished because their services were much in demand. These persons assumed the title of doctor (*artzt, artztin*) even though they possessed no academic degree. The first woman doctor to practice in Mainz was believed to have lived there in 1288,[11] while the first one in Frankfort was mentioned in 1393.[12] The Frankfort register of doctors listed twelve women who practiced there sometime during the fourteenth and fifteenth centuries.[13] In addition to these, there were midwives who had general practices as well as their special work in midwifery.

Among the doctors registered at Frankfort were numerous oculists, who were general practitioners as well as specialists in eye troubles. Jewish doctors, in particular, had brought Arabic traditions in ophthalmology to Western Europe, and Spanish Jews became widely known for their treatment in this field of medicine.[14] Three of the four women oculists in Frankfort were Jewish. Sarton states that their knowledge and practice were probably not as scientific as those of the Spanish doctors, and that they may have mixed popular herbal remedies with superstitious ritual.[15]

English women practitioners, like the women across the Channel, had to learn what they could of medicine from physicians or empirics, for at no time during the Middle Ages was a woman student admitted to Oxford or to Cambridge. Empirics were nevertheless busy in 1390, when four master surgeons were sworn before the Mayor of London to make scrutiny and present the faults of men and women practicing medicine and surgery.[16] Earlier in the fourteenth century John Arderne had

9. *Auctarium chartularii universitatis Parisiensis*, ed. Henricus Denifle, Aemelius Chatelain, *et. al.* (Paris, 1891), II, 256.
10. As early as 1239 no scholar was permitted to practice independently unless he had been examined by the bishop and an appointed board. See Hastings Rashdall, *The Universities of Europe in the Middle Ages*, ed. F. M. Powicke and A. B. Emden (Oxford, 1936), II, 126–27.
11. G. L. Kriegk, *Deutsches Bürgerthum im Mittelalter* (Frankfort, 1868), I, 7.
12. *Ibid.*
13. See *infra*, p. 143.
14. George Sarton, *Introduction to the History of Science* (Baltimore, Md., 1931), II, 83.
15. *Ibid.*
16. Sidney Young, *Annals of the Barber-Surgeons of London* (London, 1890), p. 38.

described the treatment to which women practitioners had subjected some of his patients. One of his patients, he stated, was treated half a year for an injured finger by a lady who used only "drynk of Antioch and other pillules."[17] Another, who had been "hauntyng or usyng the medycines of ladies" for a swollen and aching arm, "evermore had hymself worse."[18] Aside from practicing general medicine and surgery, women became barbers, and members of the barbers' guild. The Lincoln Guild ordinances in 1369 refer to the "brothers and sisters" of the guild.[19] Wives and daughters assisted the men barbers in their work and were sometimes included in the laws regulating the trade.[20]

Physicians in England in the fifteenth century evidently regarded all women practitioners as charlatans, for when the former petitioned Parliament in 1421 to allow no man to practice physic without having studied in "scholes of Fisyk . . . undur peyne of long emprisonement and paynge xl li [40£] to the kyng," they asked also that no woman be permitted to "use the practyse of Fisyk undre the same payne."[21] Members

---

17. John Arderne, *Treatises of Fistula in Ano*, ed. Sir D'Arcy Power, EETS, Vol. CXXXIX (1910), 44. Cf. *ibid.*, p. 120. For the recipe for the drink of Antioch, see George Henslow, *Medical Works of the Fourteenth Century* (London, 1899), pp. 77–78. Following the remark about the woman doctor's treatment of the case, Arderne described his efforts to cure the finger (pp. 45–46). He applied his powder creoferoborn, his plaster sanguiboetos, powder of arsenic, the cautery, lard and the juice of porres, more of the powder creoferoborn, another plaster sanguiboetos, and, finally, after the finger seemed to be healed, an ointment of licium.

18. Arderne, *op. cit.*, p. 49. Arderne did not describe the treatment of this woman doctor, but told how he healed the arm by means of two plasters, one of which was made of the juice of parsley, wormode, mugwort, nettle, walwort, honey, and the white of egg, tempered with meal of rye (pp. 49–50). His remedies were similar to those used by women healers.

19. Young, *op. cit.*, p. 576.

20. *Ibid.*, pp. 49–50. In 1413, for example, the Archbishop of Canterbury ordained that barbers observe Sunday more carefully, and that no barber, his wife, son, daughter, apprentice, or servant work at haircutting or shaving on Sundays within the freedom of the city.

21. *Rotuli parliamentorum* . . . (London, 1767–77), IV, 158. The attitude of the physicians was expressed by John of Mirfeld (d. 1407) of St. Bartholomew's, London, in his reference to them as worthless and presumptuous women who usurped the profession and abused it: ". . . viles femine et presumptuose istud officium sibi usurpant et abutantur eo, que nec artem nec ingenium habent, vnde propter causam sue stoliditatis errores maximas operantur, quibus egri nultociens interficiuntur, cum non sapienter nec sub certa radice sed casualiber operantur, et causas et nomina infirmitatum quas asserunt se sanare scire et posse penitus non agnoscunt." "Florarium Bartholomei," in *Johannes de Mirfeld of St. Bartholomew's, Smithfield; His Life and Works*, ed. Sir Percival Horton-Smith Hartley and Harold Richard Aldridge (Cambridge, 1936), p. 122. ". . . worthless and presumptuous women usurp this profession to themselves and abuse it; who, possessing neither natural ability nor professional knowledge, make the greatest possible mistakes (thanks to their stupidity) and very often kill their patients; for they work without wisdom and from no certain foundations, but in a casual fashion,

of Parliament were as much opposed to quackery as were the faculties of medicine. An act of Parliament in 1511 was directed at the "great multitude of ignorant persons," among whom were "common artificers, as smythes, weauers, and women," who took upon themselves "great cures and thinges of great difficultie: in the whiche they partly use sorcerye, and witchcrafte" and noisome medicines.[22] The sixteenth century, besides inheriting the professional problems of the previous centuries, was confronted with the specter of witchcraft, for most of the empirics in Europe who made use of charms and incantations at this time were accused of witchcraft and sorcery. Yet the herbal healer remained in comparatively good repute until the eighteenth century.

Accounts of some of the practitioners illustrate the variety of work in which medieval women healers were engaged.[23] Their practice, like that of the men, ran the gamut from science to superstition. Some were condemned by wiser physicians for their dependence upon charms, but many were praised for their success in healing. Since the least confusing classification of women practitioners is the one followed by their contemporaries, we shall group them according to the titles by which they were known. In French records, which prove the most fruitful in references to healers, we find *fisiciennes*, *miresses*, *chirurgiennes*, *barbières*, *médecines*, *guarisseuses*, *norrices*, *sage-femmes*, and *vielles femmes*. The terms *"fisiciene,"* *"miresse,"* and *"médecine"* were used interchangeably to refer to the woman physician who treated internal ailments. The work of the *chirurgienne* was concerned chiefly with external lesions and major operations. A *barbière* engaged in hairdressing, phlebotomy, toothpulling, and in making minor incisions. Sometimes the barber went outside her rightful domain and, like the men, took upon herself the work of the surgeon. The *guarisseuse* and the *vielle femme* used remedies of their own concoction and based their healing upon their own experience. Several types of nurses worked in the medieval period: the wet nurse, the nurse engaged to take care of the children in a family, and the one who performed nursing services in a hospital. The special task of the *sage-femme* or *ventrière* was the care of women during childbirth.

Although Alessandra Giliani was not a practitioner and cannot be classified according to these groups, she was an assistant to Mundinus de Luzzi (1276-1326), famous surgeon and anatomist of Bologna, author of

---

nor are they thoroughly acquainted with the causes or even the names of the maladies which they claim that they are competent to cure" (pp. 122–23). The editors call attention to the fact, however, that the lament was copied word for word from the *Magna chirurgia* of Bruno of Calabria (*ca.* 1252) (*ibid.*).

22. Young, *op. cit.*, p. 74.

23. For a list of these see *infra*, pp. 139-47.

Anatome omnium humani corporis interiorum membrorum and the first
to perform the dissection of a human body in public. Alessandra deserves
mention among medieval women in medicine, since she has the distinction of being the only female prosector recorded by historians. She became the pioneer of anatomical injection. According to the *Cronaca
Persicetana*, she became valuable to Mundinus because she could

> cleanse most skilfully the smallest vein, the arteries, all ramifications
> of the vessels, without lacerating or dividing them, and to prepare
> them for demonstration she would fill them with various colored
> liquids, which, after having been driven into the vessels, would harden
> without destroying the vessels. Again, she would paint these same
> vessels to their minute branches so perfectly and color them so nat-
> urally that, added to the wonderful explanations and teachings of the
> master, they brought him great fame and credit.[24]

Whether Mundinus taught other women students is not stated. Unfortunately, Alessandra died "consumed by her labors" at the age of
nineteen. Otto Agenius, Mundinus's other assistant at the time of her
death, and probably her fiancé, erected at Bologna a tablet to her mem-
ory in the Church of San Pietro e Marcellino of the Hospital of Santa
Maria de Mareto, which read:

D. O. M.
Vrceo . Contenti
Alexandrae . Galinae . Pvellae . Persicetanae
Penicillo . Egregiae . Ad . Anatomen . Exhibendam
Et . Insignissimi . Medici . Mvndini . Lvcii
Pavcis . Comparandae . Discipvlae . Cineres
Carnis . Hic . Expectant . Resvrrectionem
Vixit . Ann. XIX . Obiit . Stvdio . Absvnta
Die XXVI . Martii . A. S. MCCCXXVI
Otto . Agenivs . Lvstrvlanvs . ob . eam . Demptam
Svi . Potiori . Parte . Spoliatvs . Sodali . Eximiae
Ac . De. Se. Optime . Meritae . Inconsolabilis . M. P.[25]

---

24. Michele Medici, *Compendio Storico della Scuola Anatomica di Bologna* (Bologna, 1857),
p. 29, translated by J. J. Walsh, *Old Time Makers of Medicine* (New York, 1911),
pp. 226–27.

25. Medici., *op. cit.*, p. 30. "In this urn enclosed, the ashes of the body of Alexandra
Giliani, a maiden of Periceto, skilful with the brush in anatomical demonstrations and a
disciple, equaled by few, of the most noted physician, Mundinus of Luzzi, await the
resurrection. She lived nineteen years; she died consumed by her labors March 26,
in the year of grace 1326. Otto Agenius Lustrulanus, by her loss deprived of his better
part, his excellent companion deserving of the best, has erected this tablet."

Women doctors and even midwives often secured their training from relatives who were in the medical profession. Physicians frequently instructed their daughters in medicine so that the latter might help them in their practice or establish practices themselves. One of the greatest Moslem medical families was that of Ibn Zuhr (*ca.* 1091-*ca.* 1161), renowned because the father was a great clinician and because the daughter and her daughter after her were skillful midwives.[26] Étienne de Montaneis, a physician in Lyons, in all probability trained his daughter, Stéphanie, in the art of healing, for she was referred to in 1265 as *medica.*[27] Hans des Wolffes, master surgeon in Frankfort (d. 1393), was undoubtedly also responsible for his daughter's knowledge of medicine. She was called *artztiete* in 1394, and was twice rewarded for healing soldiers who were wounded in state service.[28] Other women learned from their mothers and friends how to make herbal medicines, and still others believed that a large dose of magic in the form of incantations or charms would ensure the success of any prescription.

The craft of the barber throughout Europe was carried on by both men and women. The work of dressing wounds, cases requiring minor surgery, and the operation of bloodletting appealed to women. Over the practice of the individual barber, a fairly strict surveillance was kept by the guilds. Because the work of the barbers overlapped that of the surgeons, the barbers' guild vied with that of the surgeons in maintaining standards within the profession. Wardens of the barbers' craft were appointed to inspect instruments, to ascertain whether or not the barbers were "good and able," and to see that they did not encroach too far upon the work of the surgeons. These requirements in themselves did not exclude women from the field. Many barbers taught their craft to their wives or to other women. References to women barbers in Germany and Italy are not frequent, and records of the English barbers' guild refer to women barbers but do not supply names of the practitioners. Twelve women barbers are named in the tax roll of Paris of 1292, however, and the names of various others appear in French records of the following two centuries.[29]

At least two women, Hersend and Guillamette de Luys, acquired sufficient training in general medicine to be called into royal service. Hersend, "magistra Hersend physica,"[30] was one of the physicians who

26. Sarton, *op. cit.*, II, 233.
27. *Bibliothèque, historique du Lyonnais: mémoires, notes et documents*, ed. M.-C. and Georges Guigue (Lyons, 1886), I, 101, 105.
28. Kriegk, *op. cit.*, I, 38.
29. See *infra*, pp. 139–41.
30. Her name so appears in a list of twenty doctors who served kings and lords at some

attended Louis IX and accompanied him to the Holy Land in 1249. Saint Louis thought highly of her services, and shortly after the expedition to Egypt, he granted her a reward of twelve Parisian denarii daily for the rest of her life.[31] Witkowski states that she accompanied the pilgrims to the Holy Land to give medical aid to the women who followed the armies and to care for the Queen.[32] As there is no mention of Hersend's presence during the King's severe illness in the Holy Land, it is possible that she may have returned home with those who left the Crusade after the expedition to Egypt, or that she may have gone to the assistance of the Queen, who at this time gave birth to her fourth son, John.[33] Hersend and her husband, Jacques, the apothecary to the King, are mentioned in Parisian records in connection with business transactions in 1259 and again in 1299.[34]

Guillamette de Luys, *sirurgienne*, was granted a pecuniary reward by Louis XI about the year 1479.[35] This is the only record of her service to the King, and, indeed, it constitutes the only information we have about her.

The woman empiric about whom we know most is Jacoba Felicie (b. *ca.* 1280), who was summoned to court in Paris on the charge of illegal practice. Jacoba's methods of diagnosis and the fact that she had received special training may lead one to think that she deserves being classed as a physician, but at no time, according to the report of her trial, did either her witnesses or her investigators dignify her position with the title of *medica*. Some of her patients made it clear, on the other

---

time between the thirteenth and fifteenth centuries, "Catalogue des archives de M. de Joursanvault," *Bulletin de la société de l'histoire de France* (Paris, 1855–56), p. 144, note 2.

31. The text of the grant, quoted from *Archives nationales*, JJ 26, fol. XVIIxx, XVII recto col. 1; and *Bibliothèque nationale*, MS. Latin 9778, fol. 210, col. 2, in Georges Daumet, "Une Femme-médecin au XIIIᵉ siècle," *Revue des études historiques*, LXXXIV (1918), 69–70, was as follows:

"Notum facimus quod nos magistre Hersendi, phisice, pro grato servico quod nobis impendit, dedimus et concedimus quamdiu ipsa vixerit duodecim denarios parisiensium per diem capiendos postquam a cismarinis partibus in Franciam redierit, in preposita nostra Senonensi. Unde volumus et precipimus ut quicumque fuerit prepositus senonensis pro tempore prefate Hersendi dictos duodecim denarios parisiensium per diem quamdiu vixerit et postquam in Franciam redierit, ut dictum est, sine difficultate persolvat. In cujus, etc. . . Actum Acon, anno Domini MCC quiquagesimo, mense augusto."

32. G. J. Witkowski, *Histoire des accouchements chez tous les peuples* (Paris, 1887), pp. 650–51.

33. Daumet, *op. cit.*, p. 71.

34. *Archives de l'Hôtel-Dieu de Paris*, ed. Léon Brièle, Collection de documents inédits sur l'histoire de France, XI (Paris, 1894), 534, 558.

35. *Compte de l'Hôtel des Rois de France au XIVᵉ et XVᵉ siècles*, ed. L. Douët-d'Arcq, Société de l'Histoire de France (Paris, 1865), p. 377.

hand, that they summoned her after they had consulted well-known men physicians. They may have consulted her last of all because the regular doctors had failed, or merely because she was a woman.

Her case was of chief interest among those tried in the Parisian courts in 1322. That this was not Jacoba's first offense, and that several of her patients were called to court as witnesses lent both seriousness and excitement to her case, features which were often lacking in other suits. The Dean and the Faculty of Medicine of the University of Paris made seven separate charges against her:[36] (1) In Paris and the suburbs she visited many sick persons suffering from serious illnesses, examined their urine, felt their pulse, and touched their bodies and limbs. (2) After examining the urine, she would say, "I will cure you, by God's will, if you will have faith in me," and then she would make a compact for the cure and receive a fee. (3) Following the compact, she would cure her patient of internal illnesses and wounds or of external abscesses. She would visit the sick assiduously and continue to examine the urine in the manner of physicians, feel the pulse, and touch the body and limbs. (4) Then she would give the patients sirups and potions, laxatives, digestives, aromatics, or other remedies, which they would drink in her presence in accordance with her prescription. (5) She often practiced in Paris and in the suburbs, although she had not studied at the schools of Paris and was not licensed by the Chancellor or the Dean of Magistrates. (6) She had been admonished by a decree of venerable, official men of Paris under pain of excommunication and a fine of sixty Paris pounds. (7) In spite of this warning and prohibition, she continued to visit the sick and administer medicines as before.

The charges of the jury and the testimonies of seven witnesses,[37] although used against Jacoba, showed clearly that she was skilled in both diagnosis and treatment of her cases. In curing every patient except one, who did not take her medicine, she showed that her work had met with success. Jean of St. Omer, a shopkeeper of Paris, declared that she had cured him of his illness. She had visited him many times and had surpassed the doctors in her treatment of his infirmity. She gave him a potion of clear liquid which she tasted before he drank it. Since they agreed that he should pay a fee only if he were cured, he paid her, after his recovery, the sum of forty Paris sous. Others gave similar testimony. Jean Faber described the way in which she had cured him. Father Odo of Cormery, a brother in the poorhouse of Paris, remarked that Jacoba was wiser in the art of surgery and medicine than any master physician

36. *Chart. Paris*, II, 257–58.   37. *Ibid.*, II, 259–62.

or surgeon in Paris. Jeanne Bilbaut named several doctors of Paris who gave her up as dead before she sought the aid of Jacoba. Jeanne of Mouchy-le-Perreus testified also that numerous doctors could do nothing for her ailment before Jacoba cured her. Mathilda, wife of Jean of St. Omer, substantiated her husband's remarks and added that Jacoba had cured the chancellor of the King and his nephew of infirmities. Yvo Tueleu stated that Jacoba had cured him also after physicians had failed. Only one of the seven witnesses, Clementine of Belues, complained of Jacoba's treatment. The potion prescribed, she said, was so horrible that her husband and the doctors forbade her to drink it.

It is noteworthy that in every instance Jacoba followed the same procedure of diagnosis as the master physicians of Paris, and that like them she suited the medicine to the infirmity. She treated the rheumatism of Odo of Cormery with hot vapor baths and herbs, among which was camomile, an herb recommended for aches and inflammations. She cured the kidney trouble of Jeanne of Mouchy-le-Perreus with potions, the fever of Jeanne Bilbaut with clear liquids and sirups, the fever of Yvo Tueleu with potions, and the infirmity (unnamed) of Jean of St. Omer with potions and a plaster for his chest. Her cures resembled those of Lanfranc and de Chauliac.

In her own testimony Jacoba pleaded her case intelligently. She reminded the judges that the law of 1220 was made for idiots and ignorant persons who knew nothing of the art of medicine, groups from which she was excluded because of her expertness and her "instruction" in the art.[38] Moreover, she pointed out, the statute referred only to the doctors, bachelors, and scholars on the faculty of the university and not to other groups of healers.[39] She made her most eloquent plea on the grounds of modesty and of the need for women doctors:

> It is better and more honest that a wise and expert woman in this art visit sick women, and inquire into the secret nature of their infirmity, than a man to whom it is not permitted to see, inquire of, or touch the hands, breasts, stomach, etc. of a woman; nay rather ought a man shun the secrets of women and their company and flee as far as he can. And a woman before now would permit herself to die rather than reveal the secrets of her infirmity to any man, because of the honor of the female sex and the shame which she would feel. And this is the cause of many women and also men dying of their infirmities, not wishing to have doctors see their secret parts. And on this there has been public sentiment, and the Dean and Masters will not deny it.[40]

38. *Ibid.*, II, 263. 39. *Ibid.*, II, 264. 40. *Ibid.*

No statement of the Middle Ages reveals more clearly than does this one the fact that women practiced medicine even in countries where university training was denied them.

The Dean and Masters of Medicine did not deny the success of Jacoba's treatment, but declared that she did not know the cause of disease or the art of medicine through letters and therefore might bring about the death of a patient by the use of potions and clysters. They took the stand of all university-trained physicians that medicine was a science which could not be learned by hearsay or by revelation, and that experience had value only when it depended upon science, which must be learned from books. The professional jealousy which must have been aroused by unsuccessful competition with an empiric was carefully avoided in the report of the trial. Nothing further was said of the three physicians whose scientific knowledge failed utterly in the case of Jeanne Bilbaut, or of the other physicians who were baffled by the illness of Jeanne Mouchy-le-Perreus. The physicians could not be expected to acknowledge that a well-trained empiric could effect as many cures as a university-trained doctor. And so Jacoba and her fellow culprits were prohibited from practicing medicine in or near Paris under pain of excommunication and a fine of sixty Paris pounds.[41] Two men, both called *magister;* Johanna, a converse (lay sister); Marguerite of Ypra, *cirurgica;* and Belota, a Jewess, were included in the group sentenced by the court.[42]

Empirics also set themselves up as teachers and accepted apprentices. Sarah de Saint-Gilles, a Jewish empiric in Marseilles, undertook to instruct Salves de Burganovo in medicine, on condition that he would turn over to her all his earnings during his apprenticeship.[43] Agnes Avesot, the maid of Jeanne Clarisse, who was arraigned in court in 1322 together with her mistress, had evidently become a sort of apprentice to her mistress and at the time of their arrest was assisting her in her healing.[44] Clarice of Rouen, wife of Pierre Faverel, learned the art of medicine from her husband and practiced with him.[45] Another empiric practicing in 1331 was recorded as "filia Clarisse, qui moratur ultra pontes, que est totaliter laica," and may have been the daughter of Clarice of Rouen.[46] Jacoba Felicie may have been instructed similarly by an empiric or, possibly, by a physician.

Jacoba Felicie maintained that she was not one of the "ydiotas et

41.   *Ibid.,* II, 267.   42. *Ibid.*
43. Ernest Wickersheimer, *Dictionnaire biographique des médecins en France au moyen âge* (Paris, 1936), II, 760.
44. *Chart. Paris.,* II, 256.   45. *Ibid.,* II, 149–53.   46. *Ibid.,* II, 337.

fatuos usurpantes" against whom the statute of 1220 militated, and her patients would have agreed with her. A century later, however, such might not have been the case, for there was a growing number of quacks and charlatans, empirics whose dubious practices caused the university men to look with greater suspicion on all practitioners outside their own ranks. The attitude of the physicians was reflected in public opinion. Joan, an English widow, was evidently one of these empirics who had suffered considerable embarrassment as a result of her practices. About the year 1400 she sent a petition to the King for permission to practice medicine. She said that she wished to "travel about the country and practise her art without hindrance or disturbance from all folk, who despise her by reason of her said art."[47] If empirics employed invocations and ceremonies that could be associated with witchcraft or heresy, they quickly aroused public sentiment which caused severe punishment to be meted out to them.

Associated with this type of empiric were the "old wives," women who used herbal medicines, boxes of ointments, collections of stones for amulets and of inscriptions for charms, to carry on extensive business in healing among the people who accepted their superstitious beliefs. Information about the old wives comes principally from the medical and scientific writings of the Middle Ages and is, therefore, for the most part, somewhat prejudiced. At no time were the old wives as a group held in high repute among physicians and scientists, although an individual woman on occasion received commendation for particular cures. These women made no effort to secure medical training. They broke all laws and regulations that applied to the practice of medicine without a license and, unlike midwives and some other practitioners, they did not undergo a period of apprenticeship. They were never admitted to the rank of "doctor," as Professor Reinhard observed, for when the patient recovered, their cures took on "the nature of white magic . . . and of black when he died."[48] With a natural bent for healing, the wise women earned their living through the application of a number of secret remedies. Since their medicine represented at best a combination of some good herbal cures and a large number of superstitions, the physicians who discriminated between magic and science were obliged to condemn them and to classify them with witches and sorceresses.

47. Eileen Power, "Some Women Practitioners in the Middle Ages," *Proceedings of the Royal Society of Medicine*, Section of the History of Medicine (1921–22), IV, Part III, 23.
48. John Revell Reinhard, *The Old French Romance of Amadas et Ydoine, an Historical Study* (Durham, N. C., 1927), p. 161.

General censure of the old wives and their questionable cures continued throughout the period and increased toward the end of the Middle Ages. Roger Bacon (fl. 1267) deprecated the practices of the women and their use of charms and magical ceremonies.[49] In 1325 John XXII urged Étienne, Bishop of Paris, to prohibit from practicing medicine in Paris and its suburbs those unlearned in the art of medicine (*ignari*) and old wives (*mulieres vetulae*), most of whom, he maintained, were fortune tellers.[50] Antonio Guaineri (fl. 1413–48) asked for lenience if his work, the *De egritudinibus capitis*, appeared to contain old wives' remedies.[51] And so it did, for among his recommendations for cures were charms and incantations, and as a purgative, a plaster to be applied below the navel.[52]

To comment upon the practices of the old wives, however, was not always to condemn them. Arnold of Villanova reported that in Rome he saw a poor woman cure a quinsy sore throat with a plaster,[53] and in Montpellier, a good wife cured a man suffering from hemorrhage with her secret remedy.[54] Gilbert of England (fl. 1230–40) cited the case of an old woman who cured many people of jaundice with the cooked juice of plantain, and told of old women from the country who gave "burnt purple" in drink, because this had occult power to cure smallpox.[55] Francis of Florence (fl. 1424–80), although he condemned the *magi*, *malefici*, and *muliercule* for their practices, was convinced that medicine when combined with magic could accomplish more than medicine alone, and on such grounds he explained the preference of the people for the cures of old wives rather than for those of trained doctors.[56] Even the most highly educated physicians and professors had occasion to turn to these women for information and for advice. Nicholas Tynchewyke (d. 1324), the first lecturer on medicine at Oxford, having read in Mirfeld's *Breviarium Bartholomei* that a certain remedy could cure jaundice, and hearing that an old woman had already cured an infinite number of cases with this remedy, rode forty miles to secure it from her.[57]

49. Roger Bacon, "Opus tertium," *Opera quaedam hactenus inedita*, ed. J. S. Brewer (London, 1859), XV, 98. Cf. Lynn Thorndike, *History of Magic and Experimental Science* (New York, 1923), II, 662.
50. *Chart. Paris.*, II, 285–86.
51. Thorndike, *op. cit.*, IV, 229.
52. *Ibid.*, II, 226.
53. *Histoire littéraire de la France* (Paris, 1881), XXVIII, 43, and Thorndike, *op. cit.*, II, 853.
54. Thorndike, *op. cit.*, II, 853; *Histoire littéraire de la France*, XXVIII, 43.
55. Thorndike, *op. cit.*, II, 482–83.
56. *Ibid.*, IV, 328, 330–31.
57. R. T. Gunther, *Early Science in Oxford* (Oxford, 1923–30), III, 9.

That some of the old wives wandered about advertising their trade is suggested in Conrad Heingarter's advice to John II, Duke of Bourbon. As physician to the Duke, Heingarter did not stand on ceremony or condone the Duke's weaknesses. He frankly admonished him for his willingness to obey any old witch or vagabond who promised him health: ". . . nam si aliqua vetula veniret vel cursores et omnium litterarum ignorantissimi qui aut propter adulationem aut propter pecuniam tibi mendaciis promitterent sanitatem, ad obediendum eis illico es paratissimus."[58]

As the Middle Ages wore on and the belief in witchcraft increased among all classes, it was inevitable that the cures of the old wives should come under the suspicion of medical authorities and that faith in them should wane. Widespread apprehension of witchcraft, however, did not develop until late. Even while Thomas Aquinas (1225?–74?) was supporting the growing belief that devils could take on fleshly shape and was writing that malicious old women could injure children through the power of the evil eye,[59] the work of the old wives was regarded with considerable respect. By the fourteenth century, belief in witchcraft had begun to ensnare the imagination of Europe, and the poor old women were thought to be actually in league with devils and demons. Dame Emma of Shoreditch, the "wicche" upon whom Piers the Plowman relied for his medicine, may have been an old wife:

And whan I may nouȝt haue the maistrye . with malencolye I take
That I cacche the crompe . the cardiacle some tyme,
Or an ague in such an angre . and some tyme a feure,
   That taketh me al a twelf-moneth . tyl that I dispyse
Lechecrafte of owre lorde . and leue on a wicche,
And segge, that no clerke ne can . ne cryste, as I leue,
To the souter of southwerke . or of shordyche dame emme![60]

Heingarten had also referred to the old wife as an "old witch." Two centuries later the old wife was clearly identified with the witch. The "old woman of Brentford" in The Merry Wives of Windsor was also called "the wise woman of Brentford" and the "witch of Brentford."[61]

No tolerance was shown to such persons as Marie de Blansy who, in

58. Cited in Thorndike, op. cit., IV, 383, note 51.
59. Thomas Aquinas, Summa contra gentiles, tr. by the English Dominican Fathers (London, 1928), Vol. III, Sec. ciii.
60. The Vision of William concerning Piers Plowman, ed. W. W. Skeat, B. text, Sec. XIII, ll. 334 ff.
61. William Shakespeare, "The Merry Wives of Windsor," in The Works of William Shakespeare (Stratford-on-Avon, 1904), IV, 2, 87; III, 5, 27; IV, 2, 100.

1403, in company with a priest, Ives Gilemme, a locksmith, Perrin Hemery, and a clerk, Guillaume Floret, called upon devils for assistance in healing.[62] The priest boasted that he had three devils at his command and that he could cure the King (Charles VI) of an infirmity, and the group declared that to prove their powers, they could break the chains of twelve men. When their efforts failed, their devices were called trumpery, and they were sentenced to be burned.

Fortunately, the cures of the old wives could not be completely identified with witchcraft, and consequently, the old wife survived the witch. Legal punishment for witchcraft was finally sanctioned in the bull issued by Pope Innocent III in 1484, in which witchcraft was condemned as an alliance with the Devil. A year or so later the famous *Malleus maleficarum* appeared and was shortly afterward accepted as an authority on the subject of sorcery and witchcraft. According to this work, the Devil visited witches in their haunts in the woods and advised them what to do. At his direction they mixed the brews and salves which could produce good or evil. They rode at night through the air on brooms, met at banquets, and indulged in lewd gatherings. The natural results of such sentiment were the trials and executions of "witches," starting near Hamburg in 1444, spreading through all Europe, and terminating only in the nineteenth century. In spite of this persecution and of her association with witchcraft, the old wife persisted in her homely cures, and we hear of her work as healer in provincial sections of Europe and America even today.

Undoubtedly, the practices of the so-called physician and surgeon and those of the empiric overlapped. One has only to review the methods of diagnosis and the means of cure which were used by Jacoba Felicie to reach the conclusion that women trained by the best physicians would have learned little more than she knew. Moreover, not every old wife resorted to charms and incantations, and doctors showed themselves willing enough to learn from the women who had demonstrated their success with special cures.

IN FICTION

Comparatively few of the women healers in fiction were professional practitioners like the woman of Salerno in *Les Dous Amanz*, or were said to have received academic training in medicine. As we have seen, the women who undertook to heal the wounds of a knight in a romance or *chanson de geste* were usually the wives or daughters of lords of castles,

---

62. Jean Juvénal des Ursins, "Histoire de Charles VI," *Mémoires relatifs à l'histoire de France*, ed. M. Michaud (Paris, 1854), p. 425.

women who had acquired medical skill within the family circle and were summoned when the wounded knight appeared on the scene.

Several women, however, were fortunate enough to have received an unusually thorough education in medical science. Queen Isolt in *Tristrams Saga ok Ísondar* and the woman of Salerno in *Les Dous Amanz* were, of course, well versed in the use of all medicines. Although the poet did not state the precise training which Queen Isolt received, the fact that she was a queen and that she could cure other than ordinary illnesses suggests that he thought of her as a woman with unusual medical training. When Marie de France mentioned the aunt's long sojourn in Salerno, she obviously meant to imply that at least part of the time was spent in studying at the medical school. The education of Josian, in *Beves of Hampton*, was probably as thorough as that of any representative physician of her day.

> While she was in Ermonie
> Both fysik and sirgirie
> She hadde lerned of meisters grete
> Of Bologne the gras and of Tulete
> That she knew erbes mani & fale,
> To make bothe boute and bale.[63]

Melior, in *Partonope of Blois*, was also remarkable for the care which had been bestowed upon her training. In giving an account of it, she said:

> And Gode gaffe me grace to lerne so,
> That the VIJ sciens I cowde parfyghtly.
> And after that then lerned I
> To knowe the Erbe and here vertu
> And eke the rotes where euer they grewe,
> Where that in kynde were colde or hote,
> All maner of spyces I knewe by rote,
> Howe in physike they have here worchynge
> The seke in-to hele I can well brynge.[64]

Although numerous women in fiction stated that they knew something about herbs, Melior is one of the few women healers who declared that she was acquainted with the qualities of herbs.

In spite of her training, Melior was not called upon to use her medical knowledge. Josian, however, cured Beves of "fourti grete, grisli" wounds

63. *Beves of Hampton*, ed. Eugen Kölbing, EETS, Vols. XLVI, XLVIII, LXXV (1894), ll. 3671–80.
64. *Partonope of Blois*, ed. A. Trampe Bödtker, EETS, Vol. CIX (1912), ll. 5919 ff.

with an ointment and "riche bathes,"[65] the same kinds of medicines that women actually used in the home. In fiction as in life, there was constant overlapping of practice on the part of the trained and untrained healers.

Herbal cures were the main source of healing by another well-trained practitioner in fiction, Giletta di Nerbona, who appears in Boccaccio's *Decameron*[66] in a tale translated in the sixteenth century by Painter and used again by Shakespeare as the principal source of *All's Well That Ends Well*. The story concerns Giletta, who learned the art of medicine from her father and resorted to her skill in healing in order to win as a husband the man she loved. As a young girl Giletta fell in love with Beltramo, the son of a sickly count whom her father, a doctor, attended. When the count died, Beltramo was left as a ward of the King of France and was sent to Paris. After her father's death, Giletta longed for an excuse to go to Paris, where she could see Beltramo. One day she heard that the King was afflicted with a fistula which all the doctors who had treated him were unable to cure. Giletta knew that this was her opportunity to visit Paris, for she was confident that she could restore the King to health. At first the King scorned her offer to help him, but when he heard that her father had been a famous doctor, he relented. They agreed that if she were successful and if he were cured, she could have the husband she desired; if the treatment failed, she should be burned.

Giletta took with her a powder which she had made of special herbs. With this she treated the King, until within a short time he was perfectly well. He then took steps to keep his promise. He informed Beltramo that, since his education was completed, he should now marry a girl whom the King himself had selected, and that then he should return to his own home. When Beltramo heard who the girl was, he objected on the grounds that her family was not so noble as his, and he asked whether the King was forcing him to marry the "female-doctor." The King made preparations for the wedding, at which Beltramo was a most disconsolate groom and Giletta, a very happy bride.

In his famous treatise on the cure of fistula, John Arderne had recommended the use of powers which were probably similar to the one which Giletta compounded. His success with his patients, however, resulted from a combination of medicines and treatment, often involving incisions. The emphasis in Boccaccio's tale lay not on the procedure which Giletta followed in treating the King, but rather upon the satisfactory outcome for which the reader is fully prepared.

65. *Beves of Hampton*, ll. 714–32.
66. Giovanni Boccaccio, "Decamerone," Giornata terza, novella IX, *Opera volgari di Giovanni Boccaccio*, ed. I. Montier (Florence, 1827), II, 113–25.

The training of Giletta by her father recalls the accounts from history of Stéphanie of Lyons,[67] the daughter of Hans des Wolffes of Frankfort,[68] and Costanza Calenda of Naples.[69] If women healers were the daughters of wives of physicians or surgeons, the women almost certainly acquired their medical knowledge from the men. Still another method of training was referred to in Chrétien's *Perceval*, in connection with an episode in which Kay's arm was broken. King Arthur, with his usual concern over the welfare of his knights, sent for a doctor, and one arrived, accompanied by three girls from his school.

> . . . un mire moult sage
> Et trois puceles de s'escole,
> Qui le renoent la chenole
> Et se li ont le braz liié
> Et resoudé l'os esmiié.[70]

The girls were obviously obtaining experience under his watchful eye. It is a pity that the poet did not add more detail about these girls, for then it might have been possible to tell to what type of actual training he was referring.

67. See *infra*, p. 141.
68. *Ibid.*, p. 143.
69. *Ibid.*, p. 142.
70. Kristian von Troyes, *Der Percevalroman*, ed. Alfons Hilka (Halle, 1932), ll. 4340 ff.

Chapter Six

MEDIEVAL MIDWIVES

TROTULA AND THE WOMEN OF SALERNO

THE WOMEN of Salerno who flourished in the eleventh century, when the medical school was at the height of its fame, were by far the most illustrious of the medieval midwives. They seem to have been the only group of midwives whose practices were so well organized that they won recognition in contemporary and later writings. Nevertheless, their exact status in Salerno is difficult to ascertain. Tradition has built up a flattering story to the effect that they became professors at the medical school and had charge of the department of gynecology. But it is now believed that they were a group of midwives who had no connection at all with the medical school, although some of them may possibly have attended lectures there. They may have been recruited, as Sudhoff suggested,[1] from the families of the medical school faculty members, and so have had a medical background. Cosmetics and gynecological problems seem to have been their chief interests. Some of these women emerged as competent individuals who distinguished themselves either for their writings or for their cures.

Bernard of Provence, who taught at Salerno between 1150 and 1160, referred in his *Commentarium* to *mulieres Salernitanae* who prepared cosmetics and to *nobiles Salernitanae* who used them.[2] At least eighteen times he mentioned the Salernitan women in connection with their remedies for various ailments. By the late thirteenth century, the reputation of the women had waned, and Arnold of Villanova (1245?–1310) referred to the "old wives" of Salerno and described their use of incantations in cases of childbirth.[3] He deplored the practice of the women who took three grains of pepper and said over each a Lord's prayer, but substituted

---

1. Th. Meyer-Steineg and Karl Sudhoff, *Geschichte der Medizin im Überblick mit Abbildungen* (Jena, 1922), p. 197.
2. Bernard of Provence, "Commentarium magistri Bernardi Provincialis super tabulas Salerni," ed. Salvatore de Renzi, in *Collectio Salernitana* (Naples, 1852), III, 269–328. See H. P. Bayon, "Trotula and the Ladies of Salerno: a Contribution to the Knowledge of the Transition between Ancient and Medieval Physick," *Proceedings of the Royal Society of Medicine*, XXXIII[2] (June, 1940), 471–75.
3. Lynn Thorndike, *History of Magic and Experimental Science* (New York, 1923), II, 851–52.

for the words "Deliver us from evil," the request "Deliver this woman from the pangs of childbirth." They then administered the pepper in a potion and repeated three times in the patient's ear the following incantation and a paternoster:

> Bizomie lamion lamium azerai vachina deus deus sabaoth
> Benedictus qui venit in nomine domini, osanna in excelsis.

Regardless of his opinion of the Salernitan women, the mere fact that Arnold mentioned them at all indicated that they had continued in practice and that they retained a reputation with doctors outside Salerno.

Trotula was the most renowned of the early Salernitan midwives, for besides establishing herself in successful practice, she is the reputed author of two treatises. One of these, a work on cosmetic hygiene, was known as the *De ornatu mulierum*, or *Trotula minor*. The other was the *De passionibus mulierum ante, in, et post partum*, a general discussion of the diseases of women before, during, and after labor. It was generally called the *Trotula major* but was also known as the *Trotula*.

A number of Trotula manuscripts are to be found in European libraries. Spitzner listed twenty-four from the thirteenth century, nine from the fourteenth, and eight from the fifteenth.[4] Dr. Bayon later found twenty-eight manuscripts of the work in English and Scottish libraries alone.[5] As yet, the oldest manuscript known to contain references to the work is one which Henschel found in 1837 in Breslau in the library of Magdalena Gymnasium, which he called *Compendium Salernitanum*. The manuscript is believed to have been written by five hands, the first two parts belonging to the decade between 1160 and 1170.[6] The manuscript contains *De aegritudinum curatione*, a thirteenth-century work which mentions *Trotula* as one of its sources. The Trotula manuscripts listed by Spitzner were entitled *De cura Trotula*, *Trotula*, *De passionibus mulierum*, *De mulierum aegritudinibus*, or *Trotula bonae matronae de aegritudinibus mulierum*. All the manuscripts begin with the words: "Cum auctor universitatis deus."

Many authorities have accepted the traditional view that Trotula was the author of this popular medieval medical work. As a matter of fact, some of them have filled in the details of her family history and have

---

4. Hermann Spitzner, *Die salernitanische Gynäkologie und Geburtshilfe unter dem Namen der Trotula* (Leipzig, 1921), pp. 19–21.
5. Bayon, *loc. cit.*
6. Karl Sudhoff, "Die Salernitaner Handschrift in Breslau," *Archiv für Geschichte der Medizin*, XII (1920), 101 ff.; and Conrad Hiersemann, *Die Abschnitte aus der Practica des Trottus in der Salernitanischen Sammelhandschrift "De aegritudinum curatione"* (Leipzig, 1921).

not only regarded her as the earliest woman professor on the faculty of Salerno, but have also asserted that she was one of a brilliant group of women who taught some of the courses in the department of gynecology in the Salerno medical school. André Tiraqueau (b. *ca.* 1480) jurist and friend of Rabelais, was convinced that Trotula not only practiced medicine in Salerno, but that she was also a native of that city.[7] Henri Baccio (b. 1609) stated that Trotula was "Trottola di Ruggieri, multae doctrinae matrona Salernitana, quae librum scripsit de morbis mulierum et eorum cura, et alterum de compositione medicamentorum."[8] Salvatore de Renzi, who in 1852–59 was the first to edit the Salernitan medical works, identified her as the wife of John Platearius and the mother of Matthias, the author of *Circa instans*.[9] De Renzi also quoted a reference from Ordericus Vitalis to Rudolfo Malacorona, who in 1059 mentioned a *praeter quaddam sapientem mulierem*.[10] He assumed that the wise matron was Trotula.[11]

More recent writers have repeated this family history and have also accepted Trotula's authorship of the two treatises. Theodor Puschman, who gave an account of the women teachers at Salerno in *A History of Medical Education*,[12] called Trotula a female doctor. Walsh held essentially the same views of Trotula's work and teaching.[13] Hamilton pointed out the importance of *De passionibus mulierum* as a source of the twelfth-century *De aegritudinum curatione* and of the thirteenth-century *Poema medicum*.[14] He accepted her authorship of both the *Trotula major* and the *Trotula minor* and called her the "medieval Lydia Pinkham,"[15] because of her great popularity during the Middle Ages. Capparoni found the names "Trocta" and "Trota" in some Salernitan manuscripts, and from these he concluded that "Trocta" was the name of the obstetrician and that "Trotula" was the name by which the treatise was known.[16] In a study of Trotula and her works, Dr. Hurd-Mead ac-

7. *Collectio Salernitana*, I, 151.
8. *Ibid.*
9. *Ibid.*, I, 152–53.
10. Odericus Vitalis, *Historia ecclesiastica*, in "Patrologiae cursus completus. Series Latina," ed. J. P. Migne, Vol. CLXXXVIII (Paris, 1818), 260.
11. *Collectio Salernitana*, I, 161.
12. Theodor Puschman, *A History of Medical Education*, tr. by E. H. Hare (London, 1891), p. 201.
13. J. J. Walsh, *Old Time Makers of Medicine* (New York, 1911), p. 181.
14. George L. Hamilton, "Trotula," *Modern Philology*, IV (October, 1906), 377 ff. Hamilton stated also that it was translated or largely utilized in two Old French verse compositions and was translated once into French and once into German prose (p. 378).
15. *Ibid.*
16. Pietro Capparoni, "Magistri Salernitani nondum cogniti," *Research Studies in Medical History*, Wellcome Historical Medical Museum, No. 2 (London, 1923), p. 39.

cepted the view that Trotula was both a teacher and the author of the medical treatise.[17] Dr. Bayon, who has made the most recent contribution to the research on Trotula, held that no distinction has so far been made "between the author or authoress of this Salernitan treatise [*De passionibus mulierum*] who is uncertain or unknown, and the matron Trotula who *vocata fuit quasi magistra operis*, according to most MSS."[18] He maintained that until this distinction was definitely established, we could accept the traditional belief that Trotula, a midwife, wrote the book. He added the conjecture that she may have been the matron referred to in the introduction as the inspiration of the book.

Doubt was cast on the identity of the author of *De passionibus mulierum* at least four centuries ago, and since that time conflicting views on Trotula have been held by scholars who have been interested in the work and its author. The seeds of the controversy were sown in 1544 by Georg Kraut, who was the first editor of *De passionibus mulierum*. Kraut was not satisfied with the accepted opinion that it was the work of a Salernitan woman named Trotula. In 1566 Wolff published another edition of the work and, apparently without foundation, attributed it to "Eros quem inepte Trotulam nominant," and called the book *Erotis medici liberti Juliae, quem aliqui Trotulam inepte nominant, muliebrium liber.*[19] Although Gaetano Melzi corrected the error in his *Dizionario di opere anonime e pseudonime di scrittori italiani*,[20] published in 1848, numerous publishers continued to assert that Eros Juliae was the author of *De passionibus mulierum*. However, Christian G. Gruner declared that neither Eros nor Trotula, but a male doctor at Salerno wrote the book.[21]

Among modern writers, Singer cast Trotula from her pedestal and banished her to fairy lore as plain Dame Trot, because he thought that the name "Trotula" was given to the work of a man named Trottus, "a Doctor of Salerno and a mere male."[22] This point of view was ac-

17. Dr. Kate Campbell Hurd-Mead, *A History of Women in Medicine* (Haddam, Conn., 1938), pp. 127–52; and "Seven Important Periods in the Evolution of Women in Medicine," *Bulletin of the Women's Medical College of Pennsylvania*, LXXXI, No. 3 (January, 1931), 6–15.
18. Bayon, *op. cit.*, 473.
19. Hurd-Mead, *History of Women in Medicine*, pp. 136–37.
20. *Dizionario di opere anonime e pseudonime di scrittori italiani*, ed. Gaetano Melzi (Milan, 1859), III, 178.
21. Gruner thought that Trotula lived in the fourteenth century. Cf. *Collectio Salernitana*, I, 152, and Hurd-Mead, *History of Women in Medicine*, pp. 140–41.
22. Charles and Dorothea Singer, "The Origin of the Medical School of Salerno," *Essays on the History of Medicine Presented to Karl Sudhoff*, ed. Charles Singer and Henry E. Sigerist (Oxford, 1924), p. 129.

cepted by Sudhoff and his students after they had studied the Salernitan texts. One of Sudhoff's students, Hermann Rudolf Spitzner, wrote in 1921 *Die salernitanische Gynäkologie und Geburtshilfe unter dem Namen der Trotula*, in which he repeated the arguments against the theory of authorship by a woman which von Siebold had offered in 1901.[23] Spitzner and von Siebold both held that if a midwife had written the chapters on treatment at childbirth, she would have dealt with the subject more fully. Spitzner declared:

> Without doubt there were women at Salerno who were probably midwives who occupied themselves with cosmetic and gynaecological affairs. They also perpetuated certain piquant erotic aids and they knew much about the hygiene of the time. They were consulted about matters of sex. We have no definite proof that one of them was named Trotula. We also do not know that the supposed author of the Trotula-work belonged to the category of the Salernitan women. In fact, it is very improbable. Of course, on the other hand, there is the relatively high intellectual plane of the book and the knowledge of the sources. It can be assumed that much of the book was already known by the Salernitan women, because they had handed down this information orally for many years. It is therefore to be assumed that the treatment at birth which is very scant in Trotula's chapter, if it had been written by a clever midwife, would have been more useful. The chapter states very briefly that if a position of the child contrary to the rule occurs, the midwife is to put it in its right place and then complete the birth. Had a midwife been the author, she would certainly have expressed herself otherwise.[24]

Spitzner concluded that in all probability, "there was a Trotula who was an experienced and clever midwife who enjoyed great fame in Salerno," but that she was not the author of the book.[25] Powicke and Emden thought that Singer was correct in rejecting the theory of Trotula's authorship of the work,[26] and Thorndike summed up the views of this school of thought when he asserted that "Trotula is no longer believed to be a woman and we have to judge the women of Salerno mainly by what others say of them."[27]

23. Ed. Casper Jac. von Siebold, *Versuch einer Geschichte der Geburtshülfe* (2d ed.; Tübingen, 1901), I, 314–18.
24. Spitzner, *op. cit.*, p. 30.
25. *Ibid.*
26. Hastings Rashdall, *The Universities of Europe in the Middle Ages*, ed. F. M. Powicke and A. B. Emden (Oxford, 1936), I, 85, note.
27. Thorndike, *op. cit.*, I, 740.

In presenting the opposing views on the subject, Sarton wrote that "it is possible that Trotula was a Salernitan midwife who distinguished herself so much that her name was naturally chosen for the title of the Salernitan handbook summing up the special experiences of her profession; it is also possible that she was the real author."[28] Since the advocates of these contradictory opinions have not yet produced conclusive proof to support their arguments and since the controversy is not yet closed, we may, tentatively, accept the traditional belief that a Salernitan woman named Trotula wrote the book, particularly in view of the fact that the *De passionibus mulierum* does present the viewpoint of medieval women on the subject of women's ailments and their treatment.

The *De passionibus mulierum* gives evidence of a wide knowledge of general medicine and of some experience in surgery, as well as familiarity with its special subject, the diseases of women. In the Preface to the book, Trotula gave her reasons for writing it:

> Since then women are by nature weaker than men, it is reasonable that sicknesses more often abound in them especially around the organs involved in the work of nature. Since these organs happen to be in a retired location, women on account of their modesty and the fragility and delicacy of the state of these parts dare not reveal the difficulties of their sicknesses to a male doctor. Wherefore I, pitying their misfortunes and at the instigation of a certain matron, began to study carefully the sicknesses which most frequently trouble the female sex.[29]

The rest of the book proves that Trotula had studied these ailments carefully. The subjects dealt with in the book's sixty-three chapters indicate the range of the author's information and experience. The first twenty-four chapters are devoted to topics concerning parturition. In Chapter XX, on postpartum care, there is an important discussion of treatment of a torn perineum, said to be the first description of perineorrhapy. Later chapters discuss such subjects as pain in the eyes, stone, dysentery, cancer, worms, swelling of the feet, deafness, tonsils, hemorrhoids, toothache, fistula, adornment of the face, and roughness of the hands. It is thought that some of the later chapters were added by editors of the text. The scope of activities described in the first chapters of the book implies that the midwife was fully aware of the problems connected with her special work.

Even modern obstetricians praise the work of Trotula. Dr. Marion

28. George Sarton, *Introduction to the History of Science* (Baltimore, Md., 1927), II, 135–36.
29. Trotula, *De passionibus mulierum curandorum*, tr. by Elizabeth Mason-Hohl (Los Angeles, 1940), pp. 1–2.

Laird recently observed that some of Trotula's remedies were essentially practical and were commendable for their common sense. In "Trotula—Eleventh-Century Gynecologist," a paper read before the American Medical Women's Association, in New York City, June 10, 1940, Dr. Elizabeth Mason-Hohl praised Trotula for her intelligent use of the medical knowledge of her day and for her excellent description of treatment for a torn perineum. She concluded a review of Trotula's medicine with the remark:

> We must praise Trotula for her keen powers of observation, for her abilities as an alchemist as well as a prescriptionist, and for her ability to write it all down in a manner which in spite of her peculiar Beneventan script, her many untranslatable medicaments, and the jumble of textual colloquialisms, reveals her to us as the first and foremost medical woman of any time—Trotula, the gynecologist of eleventh-century Salerno.[30]

Both Dr. Laird and Dr. Mason-Hohl discount Spitzner's objection that a midwife, in writing the book, would have presented some discussions with greater detail.

Trotula relied greatly upon simple, natural procedures, such as using pepper to provoke sneezing and thus bring on the birth of the child. She made use of the best herbal knowledge then available in plasters and potions of herbs; tampons, suppositories, and clysters soaked in herbal juices; herbal baths and fumigations. Animal and mineral matter was added to some medicines just as it was to some of the prescriptions of well-educated men, such as Gaddesden. Trotula's methods and medicines were naturally not so scientific as those of today, but they pointed the way toward modern practice and made the most of the surgical equipment and medical supplies known to midwives.

The reputation of her medical treatise in France and England won Trotula a place in the literature of those countries. When Rutebeuf (fl. 1250–80) capitalized on her popularity in the *Dit de l'herberie*, her good name, of course, was at the mercy of his masterful, satiric pen. A wandering herbalist, of a type well known in thirteenth-century France, set up his stand among the crowds and to those he could attract his way, he expounded the marvelous cures which could be wrought with his wares:

> "Bele gent [he declared], je ne sui pas de ces povres prescheurs, ne de ces povres herbiers qui vont par devant ces mostiers, à ces povres

30. Elizabeth Mason-Hohl, "Trotula—Eleventh-Century Gynecologist," *Women in Medicine*, No. 70 (October, 1940), p. 8.

chapes maucozues, qui portent boîtes & sachez, & si estendent .i.
tapiz; quar teiz vent poivre & coumin & autres espices, qui n'a pas
autant de sachez com il ont. Sachiez que de coulz ne sui-je pas; ainz
suis à une dame qui a non madame Trote de Salerne, qui fait cuevre-
chief de ses oreilles, & li sorziz li pendent à Chaaines d'argent pardesus
les espaules; & sachiez que c'est la plus sage dame qui soit enz quatre
parties dou monde. Ma dame si nos envoie en diverses terres & en
divers païs, en Puille, en Calabre, en Tosquanne . . . en la forest
d'Ardanne, por ocire les bestes sauvages & por traire les oignemens,
por doneir médecines à ceux qui ont les maladies ès cors. Ma dame . . .
por ce qu'ele me fist jureir seur sainz quant je me departi de li, je vos
apanrai à garir dou mal des vers se volez oïr. Voleiz oïr?"[31]

He then gave the prescription for the cure, which was an ointment made
very simply of *armoise* (mugwort), the best herb in the four parts of the
world. "De cele herbe," he continued, "panroiz trois racines, cinq
fueilles de sauge, nuef fueilles de plantaing. Batez ces choses en un mor-
tier de cuyvre, a un pestel de fer, desgeunez vos du juz par trois matins:
gariz serez de la maladie des vers."[32] His lady bade him make penny-
worths of the herbs so that the poor as well as the rich could buy them.

He warned that the herbs were not to be eaten, for the strongest ox in
the country would die if he bit one the size of a pea. The herbs should
be placed for three days in good white wine; if that were not available,
then they should be put in good red wine; or, if red were unavailable,
good clear water should be used. If a sick person were to take some of
this for breakfast for thirteen mornings, or fourteen, or still another, he
would beyond the shadow of a doubt be well cured of all his maladies.
The poet would feed them to his own father and mother if they were in

31. Rutebeuf, "Li Diz de l'erberie," *Oeuvres complètes de Rutebeuf, Trouvère du XIIIe
Siècle*, ed. Achille Jubinal (Paris, 1874), II, 58–59. The herbalist spoke as follows:
"Good people, I am not one of those poor preachers, nor one of those poor herbalists
who stand in front of the churches with their miserable, ill-sewn cloaks, who carry
boxes and bags and spread out a carpet; for such a one, who does not have as many
bags as they, sells pepper and cummin and other spices. Know that I am not one of
those, but I belong to a lady who is named Madame Trot of Salerno, who makes a
kerchief of her ears and whose eyebrows hang down like silver chains behind her
shoulders; and know that she is the wisest woman in the four quarters of the world.
My lady sends us into different lands and countries, into Apulia, into Calabria, into
Tuscany . . . into the forest of Ardennes to kill wild beasts and extract ointments from
them, to give medicines to those with bodily ailments. My lady . . . because she made
me swear on relics when I parted from her, I will teach you the cure for worms, if you
will listen. Will you listen?"

32. *Ibid*. The herbalist continued: "Take three roots of this herb [mugwort], five leaves of
sage, and nine leaves of plantain. Beat these all together in a copper mortar with an
iron pestle. Breakfast on the juice for three mornings, and you will be cured of worms."

danger of death, and if they were to ask what was the best herb he could
give them, he would tell them this one. And that, he concluded, was
how he sold his herbs and ointments. Whoever wished, could buy them;
whoever did not, could let them alone.

Trotula would no doubt have been greatly surprised and amused to
have heard her name bandied about in this fashion among the charlatans.
She would have been equally surprised at the company in which Chaucer
placed her. The Wife of Bath, in the *Canterbury Tales*, greatly resented
the fact that her husband, Jankyn, the "joly clerk," was completely
engrossed in his compendious volume which contained, among other
items,

> . . . Tertulan,
> Crisippus, Trotula, and Helowys,
> That was abbesse nat fer fro Parys;
> And eek the Parables of Salomon,
> Ovides Art . . . .[33]

Jankyn loved nothing more than

> To reden on this book of wikked wyves,[34]

and

> He knew of hem no legendes and lyves
> Than been of goode wyves in the Bible.[35]

Of course, Chaucer did not imply that Trotula, any more than Tertullian,
was a wicked wife. Hamilton thought it natural that a work of such
authority and wide repute should be included in Jankyn's collection.[36]
Dr. Bayon suggested that the source of Chaucer's knowledge of at least
the title of the work might have been the existence of several copies of
Trotula in the Cambridge library in the fourteenth century.[37] On the
other hand, he may have learned about Trotula from Vincent de Beauvais.[38]

Trotula's reputation has kept alive interest in her and speculation as
to her identity. Unfortunately, the dearth of information has led all too
frequently to pure surmise or to skepticism regarding her career.

33. Geoffrey Chaucer, "The Wife of Bath's Prologue," in *Works*, ed. F. N. Robinson
    (Cambridge, Mass., 1933), ll. 676–80.
34. *Ibid.*, l. 685.
35. *Ibid.*, ll. 686–87.
36. Hamilton, *op. cit.*, p. 380.
37. Bayon, *op. cit.*, p. 472. Paul Meyer, in "Les Manuscrits français de Cambridge"
    (*Romania*, XXXII [1903], 87–90) described the three editions he saw of *Trotula* at
    Cambridge—the 1544, the 1547, and the 1566 editions.
38. See Pauline Aiken, "Vincent de Beauvais and Dame Pertelote's Knowledge of Medi-
    cine," *Speculum*, X (1935), 281–87.

The titles of the medical treatises attributed to three other Italian women raise the question of the type of practice in which these women engaged. Their treatises would lead one to believe that they had received training as physicians, and yet nothing seems to be known of them except that they lived at Salerno. De Renzi has gathered what information we have concerning the men and women who practiced medicine at Salerno, but often we are reduced to mere names. According to De Renzi,[39] Abella wrote two medical works, the *De atra bile* and the *De natura seminis;* Rebecca Guarna wrote the treatises *De febribus, De urinis,* and *De embrione;* and Mercuriade was the author of *De crisibus, De febre pestilenti, De curatione vulnerum,* and *De unguentis.*

OTHER MIDWIVES IN HISTORY

In no sphere of medicine is the difference between medieval and modern training and technique more striking than in midwifery. The highly trained midwife of today, who works in cooperation with the equally well-trained physician, is as far removed from the medieval midwife as she is from the old wives and Sairey Gamps of a generation or more ago. Today the midwife is trained in general nursing and then takes a special course in obstetrical nursing; in the Middle Ages, the midwife was initiated into her duties by other midwives or, in some cases, by fathers or husbands who were medical men. A candidate for midwifery usually apprenticed herself to an older, experienced midwife, and from her she gained the necessary information and guidance for her professional duties. The only requisite for such candidacy was a statement from the parish priest declaring the applicant to be of good character. Since the midwives were allowed to practice as they pleased, they set their own standards, although their duties were generally outlined in books such as Trotula's work and Bartholomew's *De Proprietatibus rerum.*

The directions to the midwife throughout Trotula's book were clear, specific, and professional in comparison with the general comments of Bartholomew, who was obviously writing from the layman's point of view. A midwife, Bartholomew stated,[40] should have the craft to assist women in childbirth, in order that they might bear children with less pain and trouble. She should anoint and bathe the mother. She should bathe the child first in water, then in salt and honey to dry up the humors and to comfort his limbs. Then she should wrap him in swaddling clothes. If the child is sick, she should use medicines to restore him to health.

39. *Collectio Salernitana,* I, 372–73.
40. Bartholomaeus Anglicus, *Liber de proprietatib' rerū Bartholomei anglici* (Strasbourg, 1491), Bk. VI, Chap. X.

She should anoint him with noble ointments. Such directions were vague indeed and left the midwife largely to her own devices. According to Witkowski,[41] no laws were passed to regulate the practices of the midwives before 1560.

When problems beyond their control arose, many midwives resorted to the use of amulets or incantations. Trotula had stated that some midwives either let the patient hold a magnet in her right hand, or suspended coral around her neck as a helpful expedient.[42] A thirteenth-century popular medical treatise recommended the following incantation, which was to be said over the abdomen of the patient: *Maria peperit Christum, Anna Mariam, Selina Remigum.*[43]

Because of the lack of regulation, midwifery, perhaps more than any other branch of medicine, showed signs of retrogression in the later Middle Ages. The *De passionibus mulierum* represented the best knowledge of the period on the subject of midwifery. The gradual improvements in the field of surgery failed to affect the surgical work of midwives. Only a rare surgeon could apply his advanced knowledge to cases of childbirth, and under the prevailing conditions of the practice of midwifery, even that knowledge was not sufficient to prevent constant recurrence of infection. The midwife, left to her own devices, made increasing use of popular medicines, and brought little comfort or safety to mother and child.

Although midwives were essential in every community, it is impossible to make any estimate of how many of them practiced in any given country, owing to the paucity of references to them and to their work in existing records. They appear to have been more numerous in France, where one may have been required for every parish, than in England or Germany. Among those whose names have been recorded are two midwives (*ventrières*), Michièle[44] and Emeline,[45] who were practicing in Paris in 1292. A third woman, Jehanne,[46] also practicing in Paris in 1292, was listed in the tax roll as "la sage," and may have been known either as a wise woman or as a *sage-femme*. A midwife, Perette of Rouen,[47] figured in a trial in Paris in 1408. At first, she was condemned for sorcery, but

41. G. J. Witkowski, *Histoire des accouchements chez tous les peuples* (Paris, 1887), p. 653.
42. Trotula, *op. cit.*, p. 22.
43. Paul Meyer, "Recettes médicales en français," *Bulletin de la société des anciens textes français* (1906), p. 52.
44. Hercule Géraud, *Paris sous Philippe le Bel d'après des documents originaux contenant le rôle de la taille* (Paris, 1837), p. 62.
45. *Ibid.*, p. 114.
46. *Ibid.*, p. 78.
47. A. Delacoux, *Biographie des sages-femmes célèbres* . . . (Paris, 1834), pp. 130–36.

later she was given a lighter sentence because of her reputation as a *sage-femme*. Three midwives, the royal Yolande d'Aragon, mother-in-law of Charles VII, Dame de Gaucourt, and Dame de Vienne, were asked by Charles VII to pass judgment upon the virginity of Joan of Arc at the time of her trial.[48]

Only one midwife (*hebamme*) was listed by Kreigk among the medical men and women who practiced at some time during the fourteenth and fifteenth centuries in Frankfort.[49] Doubtless there were many whose names are not chronicled. This is true also of English midwives, for although their names do not appear in historical records, there are numerous references to their profession in medical works.

MIDWIVES IN FICTION

Midwifery was naturally not a theme that would appear commonly in the romances and legends, although it recurs in popular literature, such as the ballads and the mystery plays. A *fabliau* entitled "La Sage-Femme" was also devoted to the subject. As a rule, when the subject was introduced, it involved some unusual circumstance such as the inopportune birth of a child in an out-of-the-way place, or the birth of a child that was to be particularly important in history or legend. Much is made of the fact in the nativity plays among the cycles of mystery plays that the Christ Child was born in a manger and that He entered the world without the aid of midwives. In "The Nativity" of the so-called *Ludus Coventriae* when it was time for the child to arrive, Mary asked Joseph to withdraw. Joseph replied,

> All redy, wyff, ʒow for to plese,
> I wyl go hens out of ʒour way,
> and seke sum mydwyuys ʒow for to ese,
> when that ʒe trauayle of childe this day.
> ffare well, trewe wyff, and also clene may!
> God be ʒour comforte in trinyte![50]

Joseph proceeded alone, saying to himself,

> . . . so saue my wyff from hurt and greff
> tyl I sum mydwyuys for here haue fownde . . .
> Travelynge women in care be bownde

48. *Ibid.*, p. 81; and Abraham Jacob Rongy, *Childbirth: Yesterday and Today* (New York, 1937), p. 80.
49. G. L. Kriegk, *Deutsches Bürgerthum im Mittelalter* (Frankfort, 1868), I, 13.
50. *Ludus Conventriae; or, The Plaie Called Corpus Christi*, ed. K. S. Block, EETS, Vol. CXX (1922), 139.

> with grete throwys whan thei do grone;
> god helpe my wyff that sche not swownde,
> I am ful sory sche is alone.[51]

And,

> It is not conuenyent a man to be
> ther women gon in travalynge,
> wherfore sum mydwyff ffayn wold I se,
> my wyff to helpe that is so ʒenge.[52]

He explains his anxiety to two midwives, Zelomy and Salome, who promised to go to Mary's assistance. Salome encouraged him:

> Be of good chere and of glad mood!
> we ij mydwyuys with the wyll go;
> ther was nevyr woman in such plyght stood,
> but we were redy here help to do.

> My name is Salomee, all men me knowe
> ffor a mydwyff of wurthy fame.
> whan women travayl grace doth growe,
> theras I come I had nevyr shame.[53]

And Zelomy added:

> and I am zelomye, men knowe my name;
> we tweyn with the wyl go togedyr,
> and help thi wyff fro hurt and grame.
> Com forth, Joseph, go we streght thedyr.[54]

Joseph and the midwives returned to Mary to find that the child had been born and that Mary had experienced no discomfort. The two women were amazed at the story, and only after they had examined Mary would they accept the account of the miraculous birth. Similar action took place in the nativity play of the Chester cycle, in which the midwives were called Tebella and Salome.[55]

In the ballads and romances which mention midwives, the birth of the child usually took place in the forest. In *Syr Tryamoure*, for example, the queen gave birth to her child in the forest. A knight later rescued her and took her to his home, where she received the proper care:

51. *Ibid.*
52. *Ibid.*
53. *Ibid.*, p. 140.
54. *Ibid.*
55. "The Nativity," *The Chester Plays*, ed. Hermann Deimling, EETS, Vol. LXII (1893).

> He let hur have women at wylle
> To tent hur, and that was skylle,
> And broght hur to bede.[56]

A nurse was secured for the child and servants attended the queen as she desired.

Some of the heroines in the ballads demanded the services of midwives. Clementina, in "Willie and Earl Richard's Daughter," wailed for a midwife as she was about to have a child in the forest:

> O for a few of yon junipers,
> To cheer my heart again,
> And likewise for a gude midwife,
> To ease me of my pain![57]

In the ballad "Fair Janet" Maisie asks Willie to take her to the greenwood where she may give birth to her child:

> Ye'll gie me a lady at my back,
> And a lady me beforn,
> And a midwife at my two sides,
> Till your young son be born.[58]

Following the custom in Scottish nurseries, newly born children were washed in milk and wrapped in silk garments.[59]

56. *Syr Tryamoure*, ed. James Orchard Halliwell, Percy society, Vol. XVI (1846), ll. 444–46.
57. "Willie and Earl Richard's Daughter," *The English and Scottish Popular Ballads*, ed. Francis James Child (Boston, 1882–98), Vol. II, No. 102, B 11.
58. "Fair Janet," *ibid.*, Vol. II, No. 64, F 6.
59. See *ibid.*, II, 424, note. Cf. "Gil Brenton," *ibid.*, Vol. II, No. 5, B 61, C 82, E 32, F 57, G 33; "The Cruel Mother," *ibid.*, Vol. II, No. 20, C 8; "Child Waters," *ibid.*, Vol. II, No. 63, B 35, G 22, J 47; "Willie o Douglas Dale," *ibid.*, Vol. II, No. 101, A 25; "Prince Heathen," *ibid.*, Vol. II, No. 104, A 8, B 14.

Chapter Seven

MEDIEVAL NURSES

NURSES IN HOSPITALS

I F WE ARE to get a clear idea of the medieval nurse and her work, we
must forget entirely the smartly dressed, highly trained nurse of today, who works under the best conditions and with the best equipment
that modern science can provide. We must go back to the days of the
Crusades and of the Black Death when diseases such as the plague and
leprosy were endemic and took a fearful toll of life among the unfortunates in all the European countries, and when there was a pressing demand for the nurse's services. From the urgency of the need for her
services were born the nursing orders, both religious and secular. In
addition to the women who entered these orders and performed the
strenuous duties that fell to their lot, other women took up nursing also.
Many were hired by families of the upper classes as nurses to watch over
the children or to care for a sick member of the household. Others served
as wet nurses. More spectacular were the women who came mainly from
the ranks of the nobility and who "sacrificed" themselves in the cause of
charity and won distinction as "nursing saints."

Many of the hospitals in which the nurses worked were built in order
to care for the military casualties of the Crusades. The first of these
hospitals for the Crusaders was built at Jerusalem, and then others were
established along the routes to the Holy Land. "Residences for mutilated
men" were founded in Constantinople for the victims of warfare,[1] and in
these, it is interesting to note, the nursing problem was solved on the
self-help principle. Other hospitals, such as those in Damascus, Baghdad,
Merv, and Isfahan, were built by the Arabs, who took particular interest
in the establishment of hospitals and medical schools. People became so
aware of the need for hospitals that they founded many institutions for
the care of the poor and the sick as thank-offerings. Thus the famous
St. Bartholomew's in London was founded in 1123 by Rahere, the King's
jester, who, according to tradition, fell ill while on a pilgrimage to Rome
but vowed that if he recovered, he would build a hospital for the poor.[2]

---

1. Anna Comnena, *The Alexiad*, tr. by Elizabeth A. S. Dawes (London, 1928), Bk. XV,
Sec. 7, p. 409.
2. Sir D'Arcy Power, "A Short History of St. Bartholomew's Hospital," *Book of the Cele-
brations of St. Bartholomew's Hospital, 1123–1923* (London, 1923).

The hospital accommodated 100 patients—but did not necessarily have 100 beds, for it was customary to put two or more patients into one bed. Throughout the eleventh, twelfth, and early thirteenth centuries, hospitals and charitable institutions sprang up so fast in Europe that by the end of the thirteenth century, according to Burdett, there were 19,000 hospitals, and France alone could boast of 2,000.[3] In medieval England, the number has been estimated at 750.[4]

These institutions made valiant attempts to care for all the needy. The main types of inmate included the sick, the old, the blind, the lepers, orphans, pilgrims, and unfortunates of all kinds.[5] These patients were grouped carefully in some hospitals, while only one type was admitted into others. Lepers were placed in separate houses. Typical of the limitations imposed upon medieval institutions was the Hospital of St. Julian in Southampton, which was built for the poor,[6] or St. John the Baptist in Basingstoke, which received sick folk and wayfarers,[7] or Sainte-Avoie in Paris, which housed forty widows.[8] Consequently, medieval hospitals were designed to meet the wide variety of needs of many types of inmate, and for that reason they were staffed by men and women who were usually expected to care for the spiritual as well as for the physical needs of their patients.

The staff of the typical medieval hospital usually consisted of a warden (who was also a trained physician), a priest, and a prioress, brothers and sisters, and servants. A number of staff members depended upon the size of the hospital. At the Hospital of St. Julian in Southampton during the reigns of Edward II and Edward III, the staff consisted of a "master or warden, two priests, a clerk, from two to three brothers, from three to nine sisters, two or more mendicants [paupers] and two or three indoor servants, such as cook, washerwoman or dairymaid, and various outdoor labourers, such as carters, ploughman, and herdsmen of cattle, sheep, and swine."[9] The staff of St. Bartholomew's in London was composed of the master, eighteen brothers, and twelve nurses, who were professed nuns.[10]

The brothers and sisters in these institutions were usually professed so

3. Henry C. Burdett, *Hospitals and Asylums of the World* (London, 1893), III, 43.
4. Rotha May Clay, *The Medieval Hospitals of England* (London, 1909), p. xviii.
5. See Dorothy Louise Mackay, *Les Hôpitaux et la charité à Paris au XIII° siècle* (Paris, 1923), p. 15.
6. *The Victoria History of the Counties of England: History of Hampshire and the Isle of Wight* (Westminster, 1903), II, 202–3.
7. *Ibid.*, II, 208.
8. Mackay, *op. cit.*, p. 23.
9. *Vict. Hist.*, II, 204.
10. Power, *loc. cit.*

that, if necessary, they could minister to the spiritual needs of their patients. Their duties depended to some extent upon the size of the hospital; the larger the hospital, the more specialized were the services assigned them. The men had charge of the cuisine, and in addition, the monks assisted in religious services. The sisters had charge of the linen supply, the laundering of all hospital linen, and the care of the patients. In the larger hospitals the most menial tasks were performed by servants; in smaller ones these tasks were superimposed upon the heavy duties performed by the brothers and sisters.

Obviously, the nuns played a conspicuous part in caring for the sick throughout the medieval period. Their devotion to duty won for them the gratitude of their patients, especially in times of particular stress. The record of the Sisterhood of the Hôtel-Dieu in Paris, the oldest of the nursing orders of nuns, gives an interesting insight into the service performed by the members of the religious nursing orders.[11] In 1212 the bishops ordered that the smallest possible number of sisters perform the nursing work in hospitals, and in consequence a heavier share of work fell to each woman. Their duties were restricted, however, when Innocent V (1243–54) decreed that the order should follow the rule of St. Augustine, become cloistered, and confine its nursing services within the hospital walls. It is gratifying to find appreciation of their work by a contemporary, William of Nangis (fl. 1285–1300), who commented upon the faithful work of the sisters of the Hôtel-Dieu. "And the devout sisters," he wrote, ". . . not fearing death, worked piously and humbly, not out of regard for any worldly honor. A great number of these said sisters were frequently summoned to their reward by death."[12]

During the first visitation of the Black Death in 1348, when doctors and nurses were deserting their patients and fleeing from the cities, the sisters of the Hôtel-Dieu remained courageously at their posts, although their duties were trebled by the ravages of the plague. Doctors and nurses outside such institutions could fly from danger and duty, but nurses who belonged to orders like the Sisterhood of the Hôtel-Dieu could not abrogate their vows to devote their lives to the care of the sick; nor could they shirk their duties, especially at a time when these were vastly increased.

Not all women who nursed the sick joined the monastic orders. As

11. *Archives de l'Hôtel-Dieu de Paris*, ed. Léon Brièle (Paris, 1894), Collection de documents inédits sur l'histoire de France, Vol. XI.
12. *Chronique latine de Guillaume de Nangis*, ed. H. Géraud, Société de l'Histoire de France (Paris, 1843), II, 212.

endemic diseases spread, the great demand for the service of nurses led to large numbers of women from all ranks of society coming forward to care for the sick. This response on the part of pious women brought about the establishment of orders of secular nurses, and in the later Middle Ages these orders played a conspicuous part in the field of nursing.

Some of these women joined small orders which cared for special types of patients; others belonged to large organizations which ministered to all the sick at home. The Antonines, a small order, cared for persons afflicted with erysipelas, which was called St. Anthony's fire. The Humilati in Milan and Florence were women from noble families who devoted their services to the care of lepers. The Oblates worked with a monastic order in Florentine hospitals, but did not take vows. The Poor Clares renounced wordly things and accepted a life of poverty and service as assistants to the Franciscans. While the Franciscans engaged in manual labor or in begging, to support themselves and their sister order, the Poor Clares kept the churches in order, mended the brothers' clothes, and took care of the sick. The Grey Sisters were founded in the fourteenth century to nurse the victims of the plague.

TWELFTH-CENTURY ABBESSES AND MEDICINE

The medical work of the nuns was determined to no inconsiderable degree by the order to which they belonged and by the organization of the nunnery. The routine and discipline of the medieval monastic houses, into which the work of the infirmarian fitted smoothly, were brought into being with the establishment of the Benedictine order. Stressing the active life of service as well as the contemplative life, the Benedictines set a pattern which the nunneries followed. Where women were concerned, no little emphasis was placed upon the practical affairs of monastic life. Abbesses, in particular, came to be respected for their ability as administrators. Such skill was especially valuable when the monastic houses had to contend with povery and yet had to expand in order to carry out the duties that came within their sphere. In the twelfth century, abbesses such as Euphemia and Héloise gained distinction for their administrative abilities, while Hildegarde won fame as a healer and as a writer on the phenomena and nature of the spirit.

The competence of the industrious Euphemia,[13] abbess of Wherwell Abbey from 1126 to 1157, extended naturally to the care of the sick. In

13. A description of Euphemia and her work is given in the translation of the chartulary of Wherwell by the Rev. Dr. Cox in *Vict. Hist.*, II, 132–33.

the chartulary of the abbey she is praised for administering the necessities of life to her sisters "both in health and sickness" with "piety, prudence, care and honesty.¹⁴" She also, "with maternal piety and careful forethought," built, for the use of both sick and well, "a new and large infirmary away from the main buildings, and in conjunction with it a dormitory with the necessary offices. Beneath the infirmary she constructed a watercourse, through which a stream flowed with sufficient force to carry off all refuse that might corrupt the air."¹⁵ She added gardens, vineyards, and shrubberies in barren places, no doubt growing in some of these gardens the herbs needed for the kitchen and the infirmary. Like all practical and capable abbesses, Euphemia was especially conscientious in providing for the "worship of God and the welfare of the sisters."¹⁶

The interest of Héloise (d. 1163) was focused chiefly upon the routine and activities of the nuns. In her rôle as abbess she was faced with many problems connected with the duties of the officers and their assistants. It is difficult to tell from available evidence whether or not she exerted any great influence on the development of nursing routine of nuns, but there can be no doubt that she attempted to resolve her own organizational problems with considerable brilliance. Both Héloise and Abélard had distinct ideas about the organization and government of a monastic house, but she asked him to formulate and promote a rule which the Paracletans might faithfully follow.¹⁷ Abélard responded by adapting the Benedictine rule to Paraclet, describing each act and duty of the officers and obedientiaries so that no question would arise concerning the routine of the nunnery. His suggestions, detailed though they are, are not so minute as those of the *Rule* of Syon, but they help us to know what was expected of Héloise and the nuns of her house, and to appreciate the intelligence with which Héloise ruled.

Abélard advocated leniency toward the sick, quoting the proverb "The law was not made for the sick," and writing that they should be allowed "whatever their sickness should demand, as well of food as of baths, or aught else that may be."¹⁸ They were not to be denied meat except on the sixth day of the week and on important religious days.¹⁹ Abélard recommended that the sick be watched by a careful guardian and that the nunnery be furnished with all things necessary to the patients' infirmities.²⁰ He stated that provision for medicine should be

14. *Ibid.*, II, 133.   15. *Ibid.*   16. *Ibid.*
17. *Petri Abaelardi opera*, ed. Victor Cousin (Paris, 1849), I, 120; and see Charlotte Charrier, *Héloise dans l'histoire et dans la légende* (Paris, 1933), p. 227.
18. *Petri Abaelardi opera*, I, 175.
19. *Ibid.*, I, 175–6.   20. *Ibid.*, I, 176.

made "according to the resources of the place."[21] This could be done more easily, he continued, "if she who is in charge of the sick is not lacking in knowledge of medicine."[22] Abélard is one of the few spiritual fathers of a nunnery to state definitely that medical training was a primary need of an infirmarian. He is also one of the few to state clearly that someone within the infirmary should be experienced in phlebotomy. He did not stipulate that the infirmarian herself should be the one trained in the art, but suggested that "there ought to be some one skilled in bleeding, lest it be necessary for a man to enter among the women for this purpose."[23]

Héloise, meanwhile, devoted her attention to adapting yet further to the use of women the rule that had been written originally for men. She wanted to know whether or not women should omit the passages referring to hoods, breeches, and scapularies.[24] Should an abbess entertain male guests at her table? Should women labor in the fields, as the rule stated? Should women partake of meat and wine as the men did? The problems that Héloise raised and the solutions she offered to them illustrate her practical nature; for although her rule was pious, it was reasonable.

In the records of these capable abbesses nothing is said about the books in the library of the nunnery, and yet much of the study within the monastery or convent depended upon what lore the library had to offer.[25] The infirmarian could not have derived much help for her healing from the library of her house. The nuns did not collect scientific or medi-

21. *Ibid.*   22. *Ibid.*   23. *Ibid.*

24. *Ibid.*, I, 107–11. See Charrier, *op. cit.*, pp. 222–25, for a discussion of the questions asked by Héloise.

25. The libraries of the men's houses far surpassed those of the women both in number and variety of books. The men frequently took their own libraries with them to the monasteries, or, if they were interested in learning, set about collecting books on religious, philosophical, or scientific subjects. Faricius, the abbot of Abingdon Abbey, hired scribes to copy, among other works, many medical books for the library (James Westfall Thompson, *The Medieval Library* [Chicago, 1939], p. 304). The libraries of Monte Cassino (*ibid.*, pp. 176–78), in Italy; Weingarten (*ibid.*, pp. 204–5), and Fulda (*ibid.*, p. 67); see also Karl Christ, "Die Bibliothek des Klosters Fulda im 16 Jahrhundert . . .," in *Zentralblatt für Bibliothekswesen*, LXIV (1931), 28–29, in Germany; Cluny (J. W. Thompson, *op. cit.*, pp. 225–26), Bec (*ibid.*, p. 240), and St. Bertin (*ibid.*, p. 249), in France; St. Augustine's (*ibid.*, p. 272; and see Montagu R. James, *Ancient Libraries of Canterbury and Dover* [Cambridge, 1903]), Evesham (J. W. Thompson, *op. cit.*, pp. 304–5), Bath (J. Hunter, *English Monastic Libraries* [London, 1831], p. 9; and J. W. Thompson, *op. cit.*, p. 307), and Leicester (*ibid.*, p. 309), in England, were among those which acquired large numbers of books, including medical treatises, in the ninth, tenth, and eleventh centuries. After the twelfth century, when concentration upon learning was largely transferred to the universities, the libraries began to vegetate.

cal books, and it is significant that, with few exceptions, they did not bother to catalogue their libraries. Perhaps this fact indicates that their libraries were neither very large nor very valuable. The casual references to their libraries make it apparent that most of their books were devotional treatises.

There is doubt, moreover, whether the nuns, with their scant knowledge of Latin, could have read the copy of Hippocrates' *Aphorisms* in the library of the monastery at Bec,[26] or Cleopatra's *De geneticis* at St. Amand,[27] or the *De arte physice* at St. Aphrosidisius,[28] or Constantinus' *De re medica* at Tavistock.[29] Instruction in Latin, with but few exceptions, was increasingly neglected in the convents as the Middle Ages wore on. In England bishops were often compelled to write their visitation reports in French or in English so that they could be understood by the nuns. As early as the twelfth century, a volume owned by the nuns at the Priory of Witney set forth the Benedictine rule in Latin and English in parallel columns,[30] no doubt so that the nuns could more easily read the Latin. English nuns, in the manner of the noble lay women of their day, spoke French "full fair and fetisly," but would have had difficulty construing Latin passages. There were apparently few nuns so scholarly as Herrad of Landsperg, who was abbess of the nunnery of Hohenburg in 1167 and who wrote a little encyclopedia of knowledge, called *Hortus deliciarum*; and the dearth of medical books in the nunneries indicates that the typical infirmarian gained her scientific knowledge from the visiting physician and that she relied almost wholly upon the common herbal cures of the lay woman.

Hildegarde was the shining example of an abbess, who, although she lacked university training, won renown for her intelligence and knowledge of medicine. She was head of the nunnery at Rupertsberg near Bingen where she remained until her death in 1180. Monastic leaders like Hildegarde spread a zeal for learning, at least within their own monasteries.

Hildegarde's life was unusually active, even for an abbess. She was the tenth child of a noble vassal of the Count of Spanheim in the Palatinate. When she was eight years of age, she was taken by her parents to the convent of Disibodenberg on the Nahe River to join the nun Jutta, daughter of the Count of Spanheim, who had gone there first as a recluse, and then had been persuaded to take charge of a convent of Benedictine

26. J. W. Thompson, *op. cit.*, p. 240.
27. *Ibid.*, pp. 247–48.
28. *Ibid.*, p. 264.
29. Hunter, *op. cit.*, p. 24.
30. Eileen Power, *Medieval English Nunneries* (Cambridge, 1922), pp. 247–55.

nuns. At fourteen, Hildegarde made her professions, and after the death of Jutta in 1136, she became prioress of the convent. The fame of Jutta soon caused her cell to become a shrine for many pilgrims; and Hildegarde, perhaps in search of greater solitude, decided to withdraw to a more quiet retreat. Taking eighteen of her nuns, she established in 1147 a convent near by at Rupertsberg. There she found time to carry on an extensive correspondence with many of the great personages of her day, to make numerous visits to Italy in connection with her work, and to continue the writing she had begun at Disibodenberg.

It was Hildegarde's mystical treatises, the *Scivias* (1041–50), the *Liber divinorum operum simplicis hominis* (1163–70), and the *Liber vitae meritorum* (1158–62), rather than her medical works that won her a wide reputation during her lifetime for original and sometimes beautifully written passages on the broad aspects of the universe that so fascinated the medieval mind. She entered into discussions of man and nature, the universe, birth and death, the sun, the moon, the wind, the humors, the soul, and the nature of God. The *Subtilitatum diversarumque creaturum libri novem* and the *Causae et curae* are the two medical works attributed to Hildegarde. Both treatises are sprinkled with Germanisms which are not found in Hildegarde's mystical writings. This use of German led Singer to believe that the work was not hers, but that it had been erroneously ascribed to her.[31] Thorndike, on the other hand, states that it would have been "natural to employ vernacular proper names for homely herbs and local fish and birds and common ailments,"[32] and other scholars have not questioned the authorship of the work. Hildegarde herself stated that a girl and a man (Volmar) had corrected her writing and polished the style.[33] It is possible that these or later emendators supplied the Germanisms. There is no doubt that Hildegarde was known as a healer. Her earliest biographer, Theodoric, writing the year after her death, stated that she possessed miraculous powers of healing and that people flocked to her to be cured.[34]

The *Liber subtilitatum* was later entitled the *Physica* by Dr. Schott, who edited it at Strasbourg in 1533. Its nine books are devoted to a discussion of plants, elements, trees, minerals, fishes, birds, quadrupeds,

31. Charles Singer, "The Scientific Views and Visions of Hildegard," *Studies in the History and Method of Science* (Oxford, 1917), pp. 13–14.
32. Lynn Thorndike, *History of Magic and Experimental Science* (New York, 1924), II, 128.
33. Hildegarde, "Liber vitae meritorum," in *Analecta Sanctae Hildegardis opera . . .*, ed. Cardinal Johannis Baptista Pitra, Vol. VIII (Monte Cassino, 1882), 432–433.
34. Godefred and Theodoric, "Vita Sanctae Hildegardis," in *Hildegardis abbatissae opera omnia*, "Patrologiae . . ., Series latina," ed. J. P. Migne, Vol. CXCVII (Paris, 1885), cols. 118–22.

reptiles, and metals. Each chapter of each book describes the subject under discussion and its therapeutic value to man. The material is largely a compilation from such universal sources as Pliny, Macer, the *Physiologus*, Isidore of Seville, Constantinus Africanus, and the *Regimen sanitatis Salernitanum*,[35] but it is permeated with the observations of an inquiring mind. The numerous manuscripts of the work are proof of its popularity. The *Causae et curae* is another compilation in five books of popular medical theories and remedies. It exists in a single thirteenth-century manuscript in the Royal Library of Copenhagen.

Both treatises were products of twelfth-century medical knowledge. The author not only accepted the current belief in the healing power of herbs, stones, and words, but she included in this category other things, such as fish. Stones, she said, could cure all sorts of diseases and ailments, restore speech, and enable one to fast.[36] An emerald, for example, was potent "against all weaknesses and infirmities of man."[37] A person could be cured of an epileptic fit by putting an emerald in his mouth. Hildegarde had much faith in the virtues of the tunny fish, and she recommended taking the lung of this fish in water for fever and wearing shoes and belt made of its skin for the maintenance of good health.[38] Dimness of eyesight, she thought, could be cured by adding a drop of dew to the gall of a nightingale caught before daybreak, and anointing the eyebrows and lashes frequently with the mixture.[39]

Hildegarde also shared the belief of contemporaries that evil spirits associated with earthly things and brought about dire catastrophes.[40] The Devil was attracted to some herbs and stones but could not endure others. He was most frequently present in mandragora, which, in consequence, stimulated man according to his good or bad desires. Since evil spirits might be responsible for magic words, Hildegarde gave a recipe for a powder "against poison and against magic words."[41] And because these spirits could inhabit the air, she recommended that a woman in childbirth carry jasper in her hand "in order that the malignant spirits of the air should be the less able to harm her and her child."[42] These devils and fantasies could also be driven away by drinking water

35. Singer, *op. cit.*, p. 13.
36. "Physica," in *Hildegardis abbatissae opera omnia*, in "Patrologiae . . .," Series latina," ed. J. P. Migne, Vol. CXCVII, cols. 1247–50.
37. *Ibid.*, cols. 1249–50.
38. *Ibid.*, col. 1271.
39. *Ibid.*, col. 1305.
40. *Hildegardis causae et curae*, ed. Paulus Kaiser (Leipzig, 1903), p. 196.
41. *Ibid.*
42. Hildegarde, "Physica," cols. 1256–57.

out of a cypress bowl for nine days.[43] Hildegarde stated that herbs from the West were potent when used in magic arts and in other "phantasms" and that herbs from the East possessed medicinal properties.[44]

But although Hildegarde displayed interest in the occult virtues attributed to much animal, vegetable, and mineral matter, most of her cures were the usual herbal compounds. She knew the qualities of plants and in a list of them described their uses. *Liquiricio* (licorice), she wrote,[45] was hot and provided a clear voice if eaten in any way whatsoever. It would produce an agreeable mind, it would clear the eyes, and it would prepare the stomach for digestion. If a person suffered from madness, he should eat it often, because it extinguished the fury of the mind. *Lilium* (lily), she said,[46] was more cold than hot. One should take the top of the roots, beat them strongly with some old lard, expose them in a platter, and then place them in a vessel. This ointment might be used before a warm unguent for either red or white leprosy. Her medicine showed that Hildegarde's reading was only slightly influenced by the Salernitan school, and that was chiefly in the subject of anatomy. Her books are interesting guides to the knowledge which a person without medical school training might possess in the twelfth century.

The accomplishments of Euphemia, Héloise, and Hildegarde enable us to learn something of the way in which the Benedictine rules were fitting into a suitable discipline as far as the medical side of conventual life was concerned. Euphemia attended to the construction of adequate buildings to ensure the physical comfort of the nuns. Héloise added to the smooth running of the convent, but suited the rule to the needs of the woman. And Hildegarde, in her medical works, provided the actual cures for patients both inside and outside her nunnery. At the same time, medical care was of secondary importance; illnesses were not to be unduly magnified in a life devoted chiefly to religious thought.

NURSES IN CONVENTS

In History

Partly because St. Benedict had recommended that the sick should be given a lodging apart from the main buildings in the nunnery, and partly because it was a wise thing to do, the architects of most monasteries and nunneries designed the infirmary as a separate unit, usually

43. *Ibid.*, cols. 1231–32.
44. *Hildegardis causae et curae*, pp. 31–32.
45. Hildegarde, "Physica," cols. 1138–39.
46. *Ibid.*, col. 1140.

located to the east of the other buildings. A second lay infirmary was sometimes attached to the guest house, and here a visitor might receive medical care. In large houses with a membership of more than twenty nuns, it contained separate buildings for lepers and for patients with mental afflictions, and a common room or "parlor" for all patients with ordinary maladies. "Wherfor like as ther be dyvers infirmities," the *Rule* of Syon stated, "so ther owen to be dyvers howses to kepe hem in. One for al maner sekenes, as in the comen parlour; another for them that be distracte of ther mendes, another for lepres, stondyng fer from al other. . . ."[47]

The organization of the nunneries of the thirteenth and fourteenth centuries was fairly well described in the *Rule* of Syon Monastery, a convent of Bridgettines in Middlesex, founded in 1415 by Henry V. It professed the modified order of St. Augustine. Its rules were written after usages had become adapted to the needs of the orders, on the one hand, and to problems of patients, on the other. Since the convent was large and its membership consisted of eighty-five persons, sixty of whom were nuns, it was able to provide services which some of the smaller houses could not afford. Its size may have been responsible for the care with which its rules and practices were recorded.

The many household duties within the nunnery, the care of the buildings, the management of the properties, including farms, lands, houses, and livestock, fell to the lot of the abbess, the nuns, and the lay sisters. Responsibility for the work of the house was entrusted to the obedientiaries, who were chosen from among the older, more capable, more experienced nuns. The infirmarian was one of the most important of these obedientiaries, for the health of the members of her house was her particular responsibility.

The work of the infirmarian consisted of bathing and feeding the patients and giving them the medicines that were considered helpful for their ailments. St. Benedict stipulated in his *regula* that the infirmarian should give the sick person as many baths as expedient.[48] But frequent bathing was not enjoined upon the healthy or the young. The infirmarian was also to give meat to the weak and the sick until they regained their strength; as soon as they were well, they were to resume their customary abstinence from meat.[49] The *Rule* of Syon stated that the infirmarian should "ofte chaunge ther beddes and clothes, ӡeue them medycynes,

---

47. George James Aungier, *The History and Antiquities of Syon Monastery* (London, 1840), p. 395.
48. *Benedicti regula monachorum*, ed. Edward Woelfflin (Leipzig, 1895), p. 40.
49. *Ibid.*

ley to ther plastres, and nynster to them mete and drynke, fyre and water, and al other necessaryes nyghte and day, as nede requyrethe. . . ."⁵⁰
If they were weak, she had to help them from place to place, and lead
them to the misericord, the infirmary chapel, or the garden, as the occasion required. She was excused from her religious offices whenever
patients needed her attention in the infirmary.

The rule of the monastic houses emphasized that the qualities of
patience and willingness to serve were most important in the infirmarian.
The *Customary* of Barnwell stated that the master of the infirmary
"ought to be gentle, good tempered, kind, compassionate to the sick and
willing to gratify their needs with affectionate sympathy."⁵¹ At Syon
Monastery the abbess was to appoint as infirmarian a sister that "dredeth
God, hauyng a diligence aboute hem [the sick] for his loue. . . ."⁵² The
virtues of patience and kindliness, however, had to be supplemented by
"skylle for to do seruyse" to the sick and by a knowledge of medicine
sufficient to enable the infirmarian to manage her department with
efficiency and to effect cures in the cases which came under her care.

The menial tasks of the infirmary, as of every department of the
nunnery, were performed by lay sisters known as *conversae*. Just as the
abbess ruled over the infirmarian, so the infirmarian wielded her power
over the *conversae* who washed the patients, changed the bed linen, and
kept the building in good order. The larger the house, the more *conversae*
it could afford to hire in the twelfth and thirteenth centuries, when the
nunneries flourished. During the following two centuries, however, when
the nunneries grew increasingly poor, nuns frequently complained of the
lack of lay sisters and of the added burden of work they were obliged to
bear. At Gracedieu Priory in the diocese of Lincoln in 1440 when Gres-
ham, a nun, was reprimanded by the bishop for not attending services
at night, she replied that the prioress had appointed her to wait upon
three aged nuns who slept in the infirmary every night, and that she had
nursed them day and night, "washing them and doing all else like a
laywoman."⁵³

Three groups of patients were ordinarily to be found in monastic
infirmaries. One of these included the older nuns, who, like the three
who slept in the infirmary at Gracedieu Priory, found in the infirmary
the special diet, the greater warmth, and the more numerous attentions
which they needed. In addition to the older nuns, there were the sick,

50. Aungier, *loc. cit.*
51. D. H. S. Cranage, *The Home of the Monk* (Cambridge, 1926), p. 50.
52. Aungier, *loc. cit.*
53. *Visitations of Religious Houses in the Diocese of Lincoln*, ed. A. Hamilton Thompson, Lincoln Record Society, Vol. II (Lincoln, 1929), 123.

and finally, there were the patients who came for the periodic operation of bloodletting.

Patients suffering from "attacks of fever, tertian or quotidian; intolerable toothaches; sharp gouty spasms; affections of the brain, the eyes, the throat, the spleen, the liver, and pains in divers parts of the body"[54] kept the infirmarian busy. Cases involving minor surgery were also treated in the infirmary. Moreover, as there was no method of preventing the spread of contagious diseases, especially leprosy, patients so afflicted also found their way into the nunneries. Occasionally, mental cases had to be dealt with, and the *Rule* of Syon recommended that the infirmarian should not be angry, hasty, or impatient with individuals who had ". . . the frensy," and who "nowe syngethe, now cryethe. . . ."[55] Crippled and deaf girls were often sent to the nunneries, where their special problems added to the responsibilities of the infirmarian. The *Rule* of Syon encouraged one to believe that great patience in the care of the sick would entitle the infirmarian to an "euerlastyng crowne."[56]

References to phlebotomy are more casual in the records of the nunneries than in those of the men's houses, but they testify to the universal practice of the *minutio*, or bloodletting. At Romsey each nun was given a pittance of sixpence at the time of the operation.[57] Archbishop Eude Rigaud, recording his visitations of the monasteries in his parishes in Normandy from 1248 to 1249, reported that the nuns of Villarceaux omitted music on the days on which they were bled.[58] The author of the *Ancren Riwle*, in prescribing the life for the three anchoresses of the thirteenth century, recommended that they undergo bloodletting four times a year, and oftener if necessary.[59] He added:

> When ye are let blood, ye ought to do nothing that may be irksome to you for three days; but talk to your maidens, divert yourselves together with instructive tales. Ye may often do so when ye feel dispirited, or are grieved about some worldly matter, or sick. Thus wisely take care of yourselves when you are let blood, and keep yourselves vigourously in God's service, and also when ye feel any sickness, for it is great folly, for the sake of one day, to lose ten or twelve.[60]

54. Cranage, *op. cit.*, p. 48.
55. Aungier, *loc. cit.*
56. *Ibid.*
57. *Registrum Johannis de Pantissara* (1282–1304), ed. O. Deedes, Surrey Record Society, I (1913–15), 1261. See Eileen Power, *op. cit.*, p. 324, note 1.
58. *Regestrum visitationum archiepiscopi Rothomagensis*, ed. Th. Bonnin (Rouen, 1852), pp. 166, 194; cf. Eileen Power, *op. cit.*, p. 646.
59. *The Ancren Riwle*, ed. James Morton, Camden Society, LVII (London, 1853), 423.
60. *Ibid.*

Within the nunneries, as well as in the secular world, bloodletting was practiced as both a preventive and a curative measure.

The *minutio* increased the responsibility of the infirmarian, for unless she had not been given the necessary training, part of her work was to perform the operation of bloodletting upon the nuns. She would ordinarily learn the process from the abbess or from a visiting surgeon. Only rarely was she a trained barber-surgeon like Jeanne de Crespi, who took the veil in the Abbey de Longchamp in 1334 after she had become known in her profession.[61]

The infirmary kept supplies of linen, drugs, food, and firewood. The infirmarian needed cloths for bathing and bandaging the sick, and she had to have a fairly large supply of linen for the beds, since the ill could "by lycence of the soueryn lyghe in lynnen, or in schetes,"[62] and since they were privileged to have their bed linen changed often. She could rely upon the nuns to supply her with blood-bands, the bandages used in phlebotomy. She either had her own herb garden, in which she grew the herbs she needed for her medicines, or else she paid someone outside the nunnery to gather them for her. The infirmarian secured from an apothecary, through one of the lay sisters, the oils, vinegars, wines, and drugs with which she mixed medicaments. Unfortunately, the medieval infirmarian did not trouble to keep detailed accounts of her expenditures, but we learn from the accounts of the treasurer of Abingdon Abbey what herbs and drugs were used there by the monks during the years 1356 and 1357, and we judge from them the items that appeared on the infirmarian's list from year to year. The infirmarian at Abingdon Abbey bought ginger, wine, aniseed, cinnamon, galangal, cummin, bishop's weed, peony, cassia, cloves, mace, flea-bane, saxifrage, penidium, licorice, scammony, tamarind, turpeth, two kinds of sugar, a gallon of olive oil, vinegar, pork grease, and wine for potions and lotions.[63] Added expenses for the infirmary included fees for the visits of two doctors, for the collection of herbs, and for firewood that was used for mixing waters and oils and heating unguents. Firewood was used also to warm the infirmary and to heat water for baths for the sick or for those undergoing phlebotomy. These supplies were duplicated in the lay infirmary, if the nunnery was large enough and sufficiently wealthy to maintain one.

Though the orders differed in their attitude toward the care of the sick, it was generally accepted in all but the Benedictine order, which was less

61. *Obituaires de la province de Sens*, ed. Auguste Longnon (Paris, 1902), I, 668, 674.
62. Aungier, *loc. cit.*
63. *Accounts of the Obedientars of Abingdon Abbey*, ed. R. E. G. Kirk, Camden Society, LI (London, 1892), 14.

severe than the others,[64] that a physician was to be summoned to a religious house only in very serious cases. At Barking, in 1279, the nuns were forbidden to sleep or eat in private rooms except when they were ill, in which case they were permitted to see the confessor, the doctor, and also their father or brother.[65] The *Rule* of Syon stated very clearly: "If any suster be so seke that sche may not be couered withe oute medycyne, sche schal be brought to the crates to the physician; so that the physician come not in to the monastery in any wyse, but for a very necessary cause."[66] Medicines were to be administered at Syon "after counsel of the physicians, and precepte of the souereyne."[67] Since the principal function of a nunnery was not the management of a hospital, no particular emphasis was placed upon the work of the infirmary. An obedientiary was considered competent to cure her patients unless special medicines were needed.

In Fiction

In life the lay sisters generally performed all the services in the lay infirmaries, although some of the ballads, romances, and secular records speak appreciatively of the services of nuns and even prioresses in these infirmaries. The prioress, in "Robin Hood's Death," a ballad probably sung in the fifteenth century,[68] played a tragic part in her capacity as phlebotomist. Robin Hood declared that he would never eat or drink, and that meat would do him no good until he had gone to Kirkless Hall to be "let blood." Will Scarlet advised him to take with him half a hun-

---

64. The Customary of Barnwell of the St. Augustines at Canterbury showed unusual indulgence toward the sick: "The sick are to have every attention and all that they want; and it is ordered that one of the servants of the infirmary has to go into the town to the apothecary when required to get the medicines, to collect herbs for decoctions, and, under the doctor's orders, to make the tisanes . . ." (Ethelred L. Taunton, *The English Black Monks of St. Benedict* [London, 1897], I, Appendix, p. 305). Fees for physicians' visits are found regularly among the items of expenditure in the Benedictine men's houses.

St. Bernard had considered (*ca.* 1149) that it was "unbefitting religion and contrary to simplicity of life" for the Cistercian monks to buy drugs, swallow draughts, and go in search of physicians. (W. Williams, *Saint Bernard of Clairvaux* [Manchester, 1935]; Historical Series, No. 69, p. 70). Even more severe than the practice of the Cistercians was that of the Carthusians, who at no time sought the aid of a physician, and who were allowed only phlebotomy and the cautery as medical remedies. (E. Margaret Thompson, The *Carthusian Order in England*, Society for Promoting Christian Knowledge [London, 1930], p. 38.) There were no Carthusian nunneries in England and very few on the Continent because of the extreme severity of the order.

65. *Registrum epistolarum fratris Johannis Peckham archiepiscopi cantuariensis*, ed. C. T. Martin, Rolls Series, Vol. I (1882–85), 84. Cf. Eileen Power, *op. cit.*, p. 258, note 4.

66. Aungier, *loc. cit.*

67. *Ibid.*

68. Francis Gummere, *The Popular Ballad* (Boston, 1907), pp. 30–32.

dred of his best bowmen. An old woman kneeling by a plank over the water warned Robin Hood of impending misfortune, and other women with her wept. But Robin Hood responded:

> "The dame prior is my aunts daughter,
>   And nie vnto my kinne;
> I know shee wold me noe harme this day,
>   For all the world to winne."[69]

After asking the prioress to bleed him, Robin Hood gave her twenty pounds in gold, and promised her more when she wanted it.

> And downe then came dame prioresse,
>   Downe she came in that ilke,
> With a pair of blood-irons in her hands,
>   Were wrapped all in silke.

> "Sett a chaffing-dish to the fyer," said dame
>   prioresse,
>   "and stripp thou vp thy sleeue:"
> I hold him but an vnwise man
>   That will noe warning leeue.

> She laid the blood-irons to Robin Hoods vaine,
>   Alacke, the more pitye!
> And pearct the vaine, and let out the bloode,
>   That full red was to see.

> And first it bled, the thicke, thicke bloode,
>   And afterwards the thinne,
> And well then wist good Robin Hoode
>   Treason there was within.[70]

When Little John learned of the treachery, he begged permission to burn down the nunnery, but Robin Hood refused it on the grounds that he had never harmed a woman in all his life. He died and was buried with his bow and arrows not far from the nunnery.

Among the many adventures of Sir Isumbras, in the fourteenth-century romance of his name, was the one in which he was taken to a

---

69. "Robin Hood's Death," *The English and Scottish Popular Ballads*, ed. Francis James Child (Boston, 1882–98), Vol. III, No. 120.
70. *Ibid.*

nunnery to be healed after he had been wounded in a fight with the
Saracens. The nuns were his nurses:

> At a nunrye the knyght was leuede
> To hele the wondes in his heuede,
> That he had in that fyghte.

> The nonnes of hym were full fayne
> For he hade the sowdane slayne
> And many haythen hound,
> And of his paynes sare gun rewe:
> Ilke days thay made salues newe
>   To lay tham till his wound.
> Thay gafe hym mete and drynkis lythe
> And helid his wondes also sythe
>   Within a lyttil stownde.[71]

Since the lay sisters were free to extend their services beyond the
nunnery, some of them won reputations as healers among the villagers
near the convent. The story of one such lay sister is told in *La Jeunesse
de Bertrand du Guesclin*.[72] The sister, a converted Jewess, was called to
the home of the young Bertrand (1320–80) to cure a woman of a fever.
She arrived at the house to find Bertrand in a tantrum. Skilled in chi-
romancy as well as in medicine, the lay sister exhibited her powers. She
studied the child's palms and physiognomy, and eventually quieted him
by predicting that he would surpass all his ancestors in glory. Cuvelier,
the trouvère of the fourteenth century, who first told the story of Bertrand in *La Chronique de Bertrand Du Guesclin*,[73] merely added a conventional fairy-tale element when he bestowed on the sister occult powers
and the gift of prophecy.

THE "NURSING SAINTS"

Many women did not join either a religious or a secular order, but
because they were deeply impressed by the need for charitable work,
they sacrificed much time and wealth in helping to alleviate some of the
suffering they found around them. In the twelfth and thirteenth cen-

71. *Sir Ysumbras*, ed. Gustav Schleich (Berlin, 1901), ll. 490 ff.
72. Siméon Luce, *Histoire de Bertrand du Guesclin et de son époque* (2d. ed.; Paris, 1882),
    p. 10.
73. *La Chronique de Bertrand Du Guesclin, par Cuvelier*, ed. Ernest Charrière (Paris, 1839);
    and cf. *La Vie de Vaillant Bertrand du Guesclin d'après la chanson de geste du trouvère
    Cuvelier et la chronique en prose contemporaine*, ed. Mlle E. Dufaux de la Jonchere, with
    Introduction and notes by M. Louis Moland (Paris, 1885), pp. i-ii.

turies a trend toward a new kind of social service grew up among the upperclass women. Philanthropic work, as such, was no new undertaking for them. European history contains constant references to women founding churches, schools, hospitals, and convents. In the twelfth and thirteenth centuries, however, a small group of women were moved to devote their time and wealth to the active care of the poor and ailing, and to assume some of the responsibilities usually left to nuns and to professional nurses. The names of the few pioneers in this work are doubtless better known to us than to their contemporaries; history has preserved a record of their lives, because they were either socially prominent or were canonized by the Church. The names of their followers, on the other hand, though perhaps legion, died upon the lips of those who profited by their generosity and kindly attentions.

Mathilda, wife of Henry I of England (1100–35), was one of the first to live the life of self-denial which marked the endeavors of these women. At a time when there was inadequate care of lepers, she took them into her own home. Her brother, David of Scotland, told the story, later recounted by Ailred of Rievaulx, that one day he found her rooms filled with lepers. Mathilda was tending them, giving them food, and washing and drying their feet. The attitude of the world toward lepers was illustrated in David's exclamation to his sister: "What is it that thou doest O my lady? Surely if the King knew this, he would not deign to kiss with his lips your mouth thus polluted with the feet of lepers!"[74] Most people shunned lepers and were eager to isolate them in outlying districts of the cities. Mathilda carried her philanthropic work further and founded, in 1101, the Hospital of St. Giles outside London for the maintenance of forty lepers, very probably the first institution of its kind in London.[75]

The other "nursing saints," as they have come to be called, lived in Silesia, Bohemia, and Hungary, and belonged to one large family group. The first of these was Hedwig[76] (1174–1243), daughter of the influential Count Berthold of Andechs and Meran. Her family was ascetic, and the various members devoted their wealth and energy to public welfare.

74. Ailred of Rievaulx, "Sermones de oneribus," in *Beati Ailredi abbatis Rievalle⁾ sis opera omnia*, ed. J. P. Migne, in "Patrologiae . . ., Series latina," Vol. CXCV (Paris, 1885), col. 368.

75. William Dugdale, *Monasticon Anglicorum*, ed. J. Caley, H. Ellis, and the Rev. B. Bandinel, VI (London, 1817–23), 635. Dugdale states that the officers were first a chaplain, a clerk, and a messenger, but that as the revenues increased, other officers were added, "and also a certain number of matrons and sisters."

76. The story of Hedwig's life has been told many times. It may be found in the *Acta sanctorum Bollandiana* (Paris and Rome, 1866), October 17; and in Lina Eckenstein, *Woman under Monasticism* (Cambridge, 1896), pp. 291–96. Franz Xaves Seppelt in "Mittelalterliche deutsche Hedwigslegenden," *Zeitschrift des Vereins für Geschichte*

Hedwig's social work made her a model for the women of her family for the next two generations. At thirteen she was taken from the convent at Kissingen and married to Heinrich the Bearded, the first Duke of Silesia, Poland, and Croatia, and the son of a man who had interested himself in establishing Christianity by helping to bring the Cistercians to Leubus in 1175.[77] Heinrich granted the Cistercians funds for a monastery that was named after him.[78] Hedwig founded a nunnery at Trebnitz.[79] Heinrich extended his philanthropic work in Breslau and in Neumarkt[80] to the founding of hospitals, and it is in connection with her activities in the leper hospital in Neumarkt that Hedwig is best known. There she diligently nursed leprous women and sent them medicine or else asked doctors to attend them, "caring for them with the solicitude of a mother."[81] She sent messengers with gifts to the sick who were too far away to be visited; she offered her care to the most wretched of those around her. For her devotion to the cause of the needy she became the patron saint of Silesia.

Anna of Bohemia, Hedwig's daughter-in-law, following the family tradition, founded a hospital in 1253 at Kreuzberg and a *Klarenstift* at Breslau.[82] Like Hedwig, she tended the afflicted and gave generously to the poor.[83]

The influence of Hedwig and Anna exerted a profound effect upon the life of Anna's sister, Agnes, Princess of Bohemia.[84] After spending several years in the nunnery founded by Hedwig at Trebnitz, Agnes returned to Prague and continued the charitable work of her relatives. She remained unmarried, choosing to devote her life and patrimony to the care of the sick, rather than marry Friedrich II, to whom she had been betrothed. In 1253 she founded a nunnery with a hospital for the poor and the sick in Prague.[85] She assumed the habit of the Clares and

Schlesiens, XLVIII (1914), 1–18, examined and compared some of the manuscripts in the Royal Library in Brussels. Adolf Ritter von Wolfskron made a study of Hedwig's life as it has been portrayed in illustration, in *Die Bilder der Hedwigslegende* (Vienna, 1846). Gustav Adolf Stenzel based his account of Hedwig's life in the "Vita beata Hedwigis," in *Scriptores rerum Silesiacorum* (Breslau, 1839), II, 1–114, on the earliest records available.

77. Stenzel, *op. cit.*, p. 31, note 1.
78. *Ibid.*, p. 31, note 2.
79. *Ibid.*, p. 31, note 3.
80. *Ibid.*, p. 32, note 1.
81. *Ibid.*, pp. 31–32.
82. Gustav Adolf Stenzel, "Vita Annae Ducissae Silesiae," in *Scriptores rerum Silesiacorum* (Breslau, 1839), II, 127.
83. *Ibid.*
84. Two accounts of Agnes's life are given under the date, March 6, in the *Acta sanctorum*.
85. *Ibid.*

devoted herself cheerfully to the duties of nurse, cleaning woman, cook, and laundress for the sick.[86] Her acts of mercy extended throughout Prague.

Though deservedly great, the fame of Hedwig, Anna, and Agnes dwindles in comparison with that of Elizabeth of Hungary. Elizabeth seems to have combined all the virtues of her self-sacrificing relatives with more of the new spirit of service. In her were exhibited a clearer insight into the work which she realized needed to be done and a royal indifference to the censure heaped upon her for her prodigality. Elizabeth was born in the castle of Pressburg in Hungary in 1207, the daughter of King Andreas II of Hungary, uncle of Agnes, and of Gertrud, of the house of Meran-Andrechs, Hedwig's sister. When Elizabeth was six years of age, her mother was murdered by the young revolutionists of the *Nationalpartei*. Elizabeth was sent to the Wartburg in Thüringen to be educated. She was betrothed to Ludwig of Thüringen at four and married to him in 1221 when she was fourteen and he was twenty. Though their life together was short, since Ludwig died in 1227 on a journey to Italy on which he was sent by the Emperor, it was a busy period.

Both Ludwig and Elizabeth became active in charitable enterprises. Elizabeth built a hospital near her castle at Wartburg and daily visited the patients. She founded two infirmaries at Eisenach, one of which was for sick or orphaned children. Theodoric of Thüringen, in his biography of St. Elizabeth written nine years after her death, described the unselfish devotion with which she attended the sick and the children:

Et licet nullam corruptionem aeris ubicumque alias potuerit sustinere, infirmorum tamen etiam in aestivo tempore foetores, quos ancillae graviter et cum murmure vix tolerabant, ipsa sine omni horrore pertulit; hilariter manibus tractans eos, faciei ipsorum salivam, sputum, sordes oris et narium velo sui capitis detergebat. Praeter hos in eadem domo puerculos pauperes nutrivit; tam dulciter si eis exhibens, ut eam omnes matrem appellarent, domumque intrantem accurrendo circumdarent, sibi filialiter assidendo. Inter quos scabiosos, infirmos debiles, magis sordidos, et deformes specialiter dilexit; capita eorum manibus attrectans, et in sinu suo collocans.[87]

86. *Ibid.*
87. Theodoric of Thüringen, "Vita Sancte Elisabethae," *Thesaurus monumentorum ecclesiasticorum et historicorum, sive Henrici Canisii lectiones antiquae* (Amsterdam, 1725), IV, Bk. III, Chap. VI, 129. "Although she could never endure bad air anywhere else, nevertheless, even in warm weather, she herself, without any show of repugnance, put up with the foul smells of the sick, which the servants complained about bitterly and

Jointly with Ludwig, she founded a hospital at Gotha. The last years of her life, in particular, she dedicated almost entirely to the care of others, ignoring the pleas of her relatives to live in the greater comfort to which her family's wealth entitled her. She founded a hospital at Marburg, where she assumed a rôle similar to that of Hildegarde, the abbess at Rupertsberg. Accounts of her skillful work among the poor and the sick brought people from far and wide to Marburg to see her or to receive treatment from her. Although Elizabeth did not acquire medical knowledge equal to that of Hildegarde, she brought comfort to her patients by bathing, clothing, and feeding them. "Exercebat opera charitatis et misericordiae," wrote Theodoric. "Et quos paupertas, debilitas, vel infirmitas plus aliis oppresserat, quosque devotio plus commendabat, in suo hospitio, colligens, ipsis in persona propria humillime ministrabat."[88] And again, regarding her work in the hospitals, he wrote: "Balneatis sternebit, in lectos deponebat et tegebat, dicens ad ancillas: Quam bene nobis est, quod dominum nostrum sic balneis lavamus et tegimus."[89]

Botticelli, Fra Angelico, Orcagna, and other great artists have painted pictures of Elizabeth in the midst of these ministrations, and so have demonstrated how widely known the story of them became. It is impossible to judge how closely she was imitated in her own century and in the two centuries which followed; yet the immeasurable good resulting from her unselfish services must have inspired countless women to follow her example.

Elizabeth and the other "nursing saints" were characteristically medieval. As time went on, these women were replaced by social welfare groups such as the Dorcas Societies in England in the last century, which have since given way to highly organized philanthropic and charitable movements.

---

scarcely tolerated; handling them cheerfully, she wiped with her veil the saliva and spittle from their faces, and the catarrhal discharge from ears and nose. Besides these, she cared for little poverty-stricken boys in the same home. To them she manifested such a gentle spirit that they all called her mother and ran to meet her when she entered the house, gathering about her with filial affection. Among these she showed preference for the unkempt, the sickly, those more ragged than the others, and particularly the deformed, stroking their heads with her hands and holding them in her lap."

88. *Ibid.*, IV, Bk. VI, Chap. IV, 140. "She busied herself with works of charity and mercy, and those whom poverty, sickness or infirmity had oppressed more than others and were thereby more deserving of care, she placed in her hospital and most humbly ministered to their wants with her own hands."

89. *Ibid.*, IV, Bk. VII, Chap. V, 144. "She arranged their baths, put them to bed, and covered them, saying to her servants: 'How well it is for us, that thus we bathe and cover Our Lord.' "

CONCLUSION

From the few and, unfortunately, all too brief glimpses we are afforded of medieval women in medicine, we see them no less actively engaged in the work of healing the sick and caring for the distressed than their modern sisters are. That they labored under the terrible handicaps of ignorance and superstition is only too apparent from the record of the Middle Ages. Consequently, it was no fault of their own that they were, sometimes, dangerous ladies in spite of their rôle of ministering angels. At the same time, history and literature alike pay tribute to their practical wisdom, especially in herbal medicine; to their dexterity in administering treatment, no matter how suitable or baleful their remedies might be; and to their willingness to do whatever they could to alleviate human suffering.

As we might expect, we find some few of them trying to make their way in the more ambitious field of "scientific" medicine as, for example, the Italian girl, Alessandra Giliani, who was being trained in the art of dissection. It is even remotely possible that had she lived, she might have looked at what she was dissecting rather than at the volume of Galen—to which her master's eyes were glued and from which medieval anatomists continued to draw much of their information about the human body—and by so doing, she might have played her part in the advance of medicine. But, according to the record, she died at the age of nineteen years, and it was left for the thirteenth and fifteenth centuries to take the preliminary steps forward in scientific anatomy. Some few "scientific" women, such as Trotula or perhaps even Hildegarde, took up their pens in the service of medicine. But it is characteristic of some of these medieval figures that we cannot tell for certain whether they belonged to legend or to history. We have the writings ascribed to them, and we recognize the indirect compliment to women's ability that is conceded in the indubitable popularity of their works.

On the whole, however, women were excluded from the front ranks of medicine. With very few exceptions, they were not admitted to the medical schools; and so we find them doing most of their work as empirics, midwives, or, of course, as nurses. These were the fields most readily open to them, and they appealed to high-born ladies as well as to the humbler Sairey Gamps. Nuns in the convents and women belonging to the secular orders took the work of healing in their stride and showed considerable devotion to duty, especially in times of stress. Our knowledge of these women is almost entirely limited to the activities of a few women belonging to the upper classes and to the routines that had become established in some of the medieval convents and hospitals.

Although abysmal ignorance of the principles of medicine characterized many of their ministrations as healers, women did much useful work in herbal medicine and in home remedies. Here they mixed traditional lore with practical common sense and sometimes, as in the case of the French empiric, Jacoba, they were more successful than the doctors. They had elaborate herbal gardens, which they tended with the greatest of care, and while they specialized in medicinal herbs, such as betony and fennel, which they mixed with honey, grease, and other substances, they possibly aided nature all unwittingly and certainly not in the way they intended, by adding much-needed vitamins to the diet of their patients. In administering the remedies which they had found helpful, they were in their own way as successful as the scientific healers; but, on the other hand, they were only too willing to rely upon magic qualities of herbs and potions and upon the efficacy of secret formulas, incantations, and charms. This was the really dark side of the picture; science had a hard battle to wage against the well-entrenched forces of magic, superstition, and profound ignorance.

These women of history had their counterparts in the glamorous ladies of romance whose skill in healing is recorded in the pages of medieval literature. We find the heroines of romance called upon to heal wounds, to deal with septic conditions, to set bones, to reduce dislocations, or even to dispel madness. Queen Isolt had to cure both wounds and poisons for Tristram, while Pertelote had to deal with her husband's bad dreams. In the ballads, women had to be attended when they gave birth to their infants at most inopportune times and places. But apparently the poets did not find it necessary to go beyond well-known and everyday afflictions; for their heroes and heroines did not fall victim to diseases that are unknown to ordinary mortals. As a matter of fact, the chief difference between the ladies of fiction and the ladies of history was not in the scope of their activities, but rather in the almost invariable success which attended the efforts of the former. It is odd that we do not often find the heroes marrying their nurses. Guigemar, after a long separation, wedded, we may safely infer, the lady who had cleansed and bandaged his wound many years before. Aucassin likewise, after many perils and vicissitudes, was united in wedlock with his charming chirurgeon, Nicolette. But these are exceptions. Medieval romances were unaccountably neglectful of the tender situations which might arise in the sickroom.

Did the large and important rôle which women played as nurses and healers affect their status in medieval society? Did it win them respect and gratitude? Tristram and Gawain were profuse in their thanks to Queen Isolt and to Queen Arnive. Despite the dog-in-the-manger attitude of the professional physicians, the skill of women in the relief of suffering was widely recognized, and was sometimes contrasted favorably with that of their male rivals. Six witnesses braved the jealous wrath of the medical faculty of Paris in order to attest the superior skill of Jacoba Felicie. Since visiting the sick was reckoned among the seven corporal works of mercy, women who did so surely won the commendations of the clergy; Queen Elizabeth of Hungary was canonized. Albertanus of Brescia, distinguished judge, whose works of practical counsel were widely read both in the Latin original and in French, Italian, German, and Dutch translations, wrote in a chapter "De uxore diligenda" (1238) the aphorism: "Ubi non est mulier ingemiscit eger."[1] Chaucer, we know, thought most highly of Albertanus,[2] and in his *Merchant's Tale* paraphrased the thought:

> Wel may the sike man biwaille and wepe,
> Ther as ther nys no wyf the hous to kepe.[3]

This is the same Chaucer, be it remembered, whose portrait of a male Doctor of Physic was strongly tinctured with the acid of satire. Sir John Paston had a justifiable faith in his wife's *flose ungwentorum*, and the family's experience with physicians of London, as Margaret Paston testified, had been disillusioning.

An extraordinary testimony to the influence which women might be expected to wield through a knowledge of medicine is furnished by Pierre Dubois, one of the most original thinkers of the Middle Ages. In his *De recuperatione Terrae Sanctae* (1306), which he addressed to Edward I of England and Philippe le Bel of France, he proposed that clever and attractive women be educated as medical missionaries and sent to the Orient.[4]

> Puelle in medicina et cerurgia cum antecedentibus ad hec neccessariis instruantur . . . ut convenienter possint majoribus principibus, clericis, et aliis ditioribus Orientalibus in uxores dari . . . per quas sic litteratas, articulos et sacramenta more romano credentes, liberos

---

1. *Archiv für das Studium der neueren Sprachen und Literaturen*, LXXXVI (1891), 42.
2. W. W. Lawrence, "The Tale of Melibeus," *Essays and Studies in Honor of Carleton Brown* (New York, 1940), pp. 100 ff.
3. Geoffrey Chaucer, "The Merchant's Tale," in *The Complete Works of Geoffrey Chaucer*, ed. F. N. Robinson (Cambridge, Mass., 1933), ll. 1381 ff.
4. G. G. Coulton, *Medieval Panorama* (Cambridge and New York, 1938), p. 624.

suos et maritos ad sic tenendum, credendum, et sacrificandum contingeret informari longe forcioribus rationibus et occasionibus illis, que per consilium mulierum induxerunt Salomonem, summum sapientem, ad ydolatrandum. Iste propter terre natalis affectionem procurarent multas puellas de hujusmodi provisione studiorum cum filiis suis et aliis terre majoribus maritari; . . . incolas illorum locorum ad ritum romanum per hoc inducentes paulatim, presertim mulieres quibus iste per exercitium medicine et cerurgie subvenirent, presertim in secretis infirmitatibus et neccessitatibus earum; contingere non posset verisimiliter quin iste nobiliores et ditiores aliis matronis, medicine et cerurgie ac experimentorum que sciri possent ubique noticiam habentes, matronas earum consiliis indigentes, prudencias earum sibi proficuas admirantes, propter hec eas diligentes, fortiter attraherent ad communicandum cum ipsis, delectandum et conveniendum in articulis et sacramentis.[5]

This proposal was far too daring and intelligent to interest the warrior kings, and nothing came of it. But it is significant. Dubois's observations had evidently convinced him that much of the influence which women wielded in his world was due to their reputation as healers. His scheme is perhaps the most striking testimony we have that the ministrations of medieval women to the sick, however amateurish or even mistaken by modern standards, were sufficiently successful to win them the gratitude, the devotion, and the respect of their contemporaries.

5. Pierre Dubois, *De recuperatione Terre Sancte*, ed. Ch.—V. Langlois (Paris, 1891), pp. 51 f. (Cf. also pp. 70 f.) "Let maidens be instructed in medicine and surgery along with preliminary training necessary for these studies . . . so that when desirable they may be given in matrimony to the higher princes, the clergy, and the other wealthier men of the East. . . . Through these maidens, thus educated, believing in the articles of faith and the sacraments according to the Roman use, it may come about that their children and their husbands would be instructed to hold the tenets and observe the sacraments in this wise by far stronger reasons and causes than those which led Solomon, the supreme sage, to idolatry. Let these women because of their love for their native land secure many maidens equipped with this sort of education as brides for their sons and other great men of the country . . . gradually winning over the inhabitants of these places to the Roman rite by this method, especially the women with whom they may come in contact through the practice of medicine and surgery, above all in their secret infirmities and needs. It could not fail to come about that these women, nobler and richer than other matrons, enjoying a reputation everywhere in medicine and surgery and such experiments as could be known, would strongly attract those matrons who, needing their advice, would admire their wisdom so beneficial to them and would love them for these reasons, so that they would communicate with them and delight and agree in the articles of faith and the sacraments."

Appendix I

WOMEN PRACTITIONERS OF THE LATER MIDDLE AGES

THE NAMES of many of the women practitioners who lived between 1100 and 1500 are listed below. To present a complete list of women healers of the period would be almost impossible, since much source material is unavailable. The healers are classified according to the type of work in which they were engaged and the country in which they lived. The women who were not called barbers, physicians, surgeons, nurses, or midwives are classified as empirics. I have retained the spelling of the names as I found them in the source material.

Because the same sources appear frequently in the references, I have used the following abbreviations:

Chart. Paris: Auctarium chartularii universitatis parisiensis, ed. Henricus Denifle, Aemilius Chatelain, *et al.* (Paris, 1894–1938).

Géraud: Hercule Géraud, *Paris sous Philippe le Bel d'après des documents originaux contenant le rôle de la taille* (Paris, 1837).

Kriegk: G. L. Kriegk, *Deutsches Bürgerthum im Mittelalter* (Frankfort, 1868).

Lipinska: Mélanie Lipinska, *Histoire des femmes médecins* (Paris, 1900).

Wickersheimer: Ernest Wickersheimer, *Dictionnaire biographique des médecins en France au moyen âge* (Paris, 1936).

BARBERS

France

1256 Marie (*barbitonsorie*). Mentioned in census of St. Spire de Corbeil. *Cartulaire de Saint-Spire de Corbeil*, ed. E. Coüard-Luys (Rambouillet, 1882), p. 132; Wickersheimer, II, 537.

1284 Marianne (*barbériesse*). Douai. Wife of Jean de Montigny. A band of ruffians from Lille stole and burned her sign and caused considerable damage in the town. H. R. Duthilloeul, *Douai et Lille au XIII° siècle* (Douai, 1850), pp. 11–12; Wickersheimer, II, 537.

1291 Théophanie (*barbitontrice*). Paris. Her name appears in a long list of those who, for some unstated reason, caused trouble. *Mélanges historiques . . . Collection de documents inédits sur l'histoire de France* (Paris, 1877), II, 273; Wickersheimer, II, 750.

1292 *La petite barbière*. Paris, parish of Saint-Gervais. Géraud, p. 108.

Aales (*barbière*). Paris, Rue des Escoufles. *Ibid.*, p. 114; Wickersheimer, I, 1.

Aalis (*barbière*). Paris, parish of Saint Séverin de Petit Point. Géraud, p. 150; Wickersheimer, I, 1.

Aveline (*barbière*). Géraud, p. 53; Godefroy de Paris, *Chronique métrique suivie de la taille de Paris en 1313*, ed. J. A. Buchon (Paris, 1827), p. 64; Wickersheimer, I, 56.

Denise (*barbière*). Paris, parish of Saint-Germain-l'Auxerrois. Géraud, p. 31; Wickersheimer, I, 17.

Edeline (*barbière*). Paris, Rue au Fuerre. Géraud, p. 47; Wickersheimer, I, 144.

Dame Emengart (*barbière*). Paris, parish of Saint-Séverin. Géraud, p. 154; Wickersheimer, I, 129.

Eudeline (*barbière*). Paris, Rue Saint-Christofle. Géraud, p. 147; Wickersheimer, I, 144.

Marie (*barbière*). Paris, Ruelle Saint-Jehan. Géraud, p. 116; Wickersheimer, II, 537.

Marie (*barbière*). Paris, Rue aux Escrivains. Géraud, p. 157; Wickersheimer, II, 537.

Savoureuse (*barbière*). Paris, Rue Neuve. Géraud, p. 83.

Ysabiau (*barbière*). Paris, Rue Saint-Germain. Géraud, p. 29; Wickersheimer, I, 312.

1310 Marguerite (*barbière*). Pas-de-Calais. She received 6s. from the Comtesse d'Artois for healing little Pieret's head. Wickersheimer, II, 537.

1334 Jeanne de Crespi (*barbière*). She took the veil at the Abbey of Longchamp and died there in 1349. *Obituaires de la province de Sens*, ed. Auguste Longnon (Paris, 1902), I[1], 668, 672, 674; Wickersheimer, II, 505.

1335 Perronnelle (*barbière*). Paris. She owned a house on the Rue Saint Jacques, on which Philippe VI redeemed the rent for Pierre des Essors so that he might found two chapels in the church of Saint-Germain l'Auxerrois. *Documents parisiens du règne de Philippe VI de Valois*, ed. Jules Viard (Paris, 1899), I, 232.

1344 Marie (*barbière*). Reims. Wickersheimer, II, 538.

1412–16 Jehannette la Mareschaude (*barbière*). Reims. *Ibid.*, II, 506.

1421 Jeannette Du Fossé (*barbière*). Paris. She paid a tax of two ounces. *Choix de pièces inédites relatives au règne de Charles VI*, ed. L. Douët-d'Arcq, Société de l'Histoire de France, I (Paris, 1863), 419; Wickersheimer, II, 506.

1438 Jeanne de Cusey (*barbière*). Dijon. Wife of Girart de Cusey, who was arrested for meddling with surgery and medicine, from which he was prohibited under pain of banishment. Wickersheimer, II, 505–6.

DOCTORS

France

1250 Hersend (*phisice*). Paris. Wife of Jacques, apothecary to the King. Hersend herself was in the service of Louis IX and accompanied him to the Holy Land. See "Catalogue des archives de M. de Joursanvault," *Bulletin de la Société de l'Histoire de France* (Paris, 1855–56), p. 144, note 2; *Archives de l'Hôtel-Dieu de Paris*, ed. Léon Brièle (Paris, 1894), XI, 534, 535, 538; and Georges Daumet, "Une femme—médecin au XIII° siècle," *Revue des Études historiques*, LXXXIV (1918), 69–71.

1265 Stéphanie (*medica*). Lyons. Daughter of a doctor, Étienne de Montanéis. *Bibliothèque historique du Lyonnais, mémoires, notes et documents* . . ., ed. M.-C. and Georges Guigue (Lyons, 1886), I, 101, 105; Wickersheimer, II, 747.

1292 Haoys (*meresse*). Paris, Ville de Saint-Lorenz. Géraud, p. 61.
Dame Heloys (*miergesse*). Paris, Rue des Jardins. *Ibid.*, p. 134.
Marie (*meresse*). Paris, near l'Hôpital de Lourcine. Géraud, p. 173; Wickersheimer, II, 538.
Phelippe (*miergesse*). Paris, Rue Gervèse-Loharenc. Géraud, p. 138.
Richeut (*meresse*). Paris, Parish of Saint-Gervais. *Ibid.*, p. 108.
Sarre (*mirgesse*). Paris, a l'Attacherie. Géraud, p. 179. Daughter of *sieur* Vivant and mother of a daughter, Florian, who was also practicing medicine. Lipinska, 118.
Ysabel (*meresse*). Paris, Rue de Frépillon. Géraud, p. 65; Wickersheimer, II, 312.
Ysabiau (*mirgesse*). Paris, parish of Saint-Oportune. Her name appears in the tax roll of 1292. Géraud, p. 57; Wickersheimer, I, 312.

1303 Adine (*mirausse*). Aube. *Dictionnaire de l'ancienne langue française et de tous ses dialectes du IX° au XV° siècle*, ed. Frédéric Eugène Godefroy (Paris, 1880–1902), V, 341.

1313 Ameline (*miresse*). Paris, Rue Guillaume Porée. She was practicing medicine in Paris in 1313. Godefroy de Paris (*op. cit.*), II, 20. Between 1324 and 1325 she was arraigned in court for practicing illegally. *Chart*, II, 256; Wickersheimer, I, 21.

1397–1400 Marie de Gy (*physicienne*). Dijon. Wife of François de Gy, barber. When a patient died at her home, she was excommunicated. Wickersheimer, II, 538.

1435 Isabelle (*physicienne*). Fécamp. *Ibid.*, I, 312.

1446–48 Jehanette (*la physicienne, alias Princesse*). Lyons, *Ibid.*, II, 506.

1449 Biatris (*metgessa*). Montpellier. *Ibid.*, II, 784.

1463 Bertrande. Avignon, Rue Calade. In 1463 she received 2*s.* for giving medicine to a poor person from l'Hôpital de Cor-Sant. *Ibid.*, I, 84.

15c. Jeanne de Chailly (*médecine*). Lyons. *Ibid.*, I, 96; II, 505.

Italy

ca. 1220 Ghilietta (*medica*). Pinerolo. She is named in a statute of the town. Lipinska, p. 148.

? Adelmota Maltranersa. Naples. Obtained royal permission to practice medicine. *Ibid.*, p. 149.

? Marguerita. Naples. Obtained royal permission to practice medicine. *Ibid.*, p. 149.

ca. 1300 Beatrice. Venice. Widow of Gherardo di Candia. *Ibid.*, p. 148.

1304 Jacobina (*medica*). Bologna. She was called "filia quondam Bartolomei medica." *Ibid.*, p. 150.

14c. Leonetta (*medica*). Turin. Wife of Giovanni di Gorzano. *Ibid.*, p. 148.

Between 1386 and 1408 Maestra Antonia. Florence. Matriculated in medicine; wife of Maestro Daniello. *Ibid.*, p. 148.

1423 Costanza Calenda. Naples. Lectured on medicine *ex cathedra* during the reign of John of Anjou. Lipinska, pp. 99–100. Her father, Salvator Calenda, was dean of the Faculty of Medicine at Salerno. Costanza was said to have won special honors in her medical examination. *Collectio Salernitana*, ed. Salvatore de Renzi (Naples, 1852–59), I, 372.

1430 Luise Trentacapilli. Salerno. *Collectio Salernitana*, I, 373.

15c. Catherina (*medica di casa*). Hospital of Sancta—Maria—Nuova. The reference to her is found in the library of Magliobecchi in a book of receipts. Lipinska, 149.

Jacopa. Practiced in year of the pestilence, 1474. She is referred to in the register of Magliobecchi. *Ibid.*, p. 149.

Germany

1288 Anonymous doctor. Mainz. Kriegk, I, 7; Lipinska, p. 123.

1393 Anonymous doctor. Frankfort. Kriegk, I, 7; Lipinska, p. 123.

1394 Daughter of the doctor and surgeon Hans des Wolffes. Frankfort. She was honored twice by the city for her healing of soldiers. Kriegk, I, 38; Lipinska, p. 123.

1397 Hebel. Kriegk, I, 39; Lipinska, p. 123.

14c. Agnes. Strasbourg. Wickersheimer, I, 10.

1419 Sara. Wartzburg. Johann II gave her permission to practice in the bishopric of Wartzburg if she paid an annual tax of ten florins. Lipinska, pp. 123, 124.

1423 Anonymous doctor and oculist (*ercztin* and *auginercztin*). Frankfort. She was still practicing in 1427. Kriegk, I, 41; Lipinska, p. 123.

1428 Serlin. Frankfort. Jewish oculist. Kriegk, I, 42; Lipinska, p. 123.

1433 Anonymous Jewish doctor. Frankfort. Kriegk, I, 43; Lipinska, p. 123.

1435 Anonymous Jewish doctor. Frankfort. Kriegk, I, 43; Lipinska, p. 123.

1439 Anonymous Jewish doctor. Frankfort. Kriegk, I, 44; Lipinska, p. 123.

1446 Anonymous Jewish oculist. Frankfort. Kriegk, I, 44; Lipinska, p. 123.

1457 Anonymous Jewish doctor. Frankfort. She was permitted to remain in the city only if she paid the nightly tax. Kriegk, I, 45.

1492-99 Anonymous Jewish doctor. Frankfort. She was refused permission to live outside the Jewish quarter. Kriegk, I, 50; Lipinska, p. 124.

1495 An old doctor (*die alt artzethin*). Frankfort. Kriegk, I, 51; Lipinska, p. 124.

SURGEONS

France

1312 Gertrude (*chirurgienne*). Obernai. Her son, Henry, a priest, is mentioned in 1312. Wickersheimer, I, 189.

1322 Marguerite de Ypra (*cirurgica*). Paris. She was prohibited from practicing medicine under pain of excommunication and a fine of 60£. *Chart.*, II, 267.

14c. Marguerite la Chopillarde (*sirurgicarum*). August 8 is given as the anniversary of her death in the obituaries of the chaplains of Notre-Dame de Paris. *Obituaires de la province de Sens*, I, 236; Wickersheimer, II, 537.

1366 Jeanne d'Auxerre. She died at Chalon-sur-Saône. Wickersheimer, II, 505.

1479 Guillemette Du Luys. Paris. In the service of Louis XI, she had special charge of some of the baths. About 1479 she was given 19£. 5s. t. for her services to the King. "Comptes de l'Hôtel des Rois de France," ed. L. Douët-d'Arcq (Paris, 1865), *Mémoires de la Société historique, littéraire et scientifique du Cher*, XXI (1906–07), 75; Wickersheimer, I, 267.

Italy

1321 Francesca. Salerno. Wife of Matteo de Romana. She received a public certificate from the University of Salerno, stating that she possessed knowledge of surgery and had passed an examination before a commission of doctors and surgeons. Lipinska, p. 99.

EMPIRICS

France

ca. 1200 Laurette de Saint-Valéry. Amiens. Wife of Aléaume de Fontaines. She had a great reputation for charity, and she learned medicine in order to care for the poor. *Dictionnaire de biographie française*, ed. J. Balteau (Paris, 1933), I, 1374; Wickersheimer, II, 522.

13c. Arnaude. A heretic of the Catharist sect. She attended Arpais, daughter of Assaut, Lady du Mas, for a period of two weeks or so. The Cathari had their own doctors, and both men and women were healers. Wickersheimer, I, 49.

1312 Clarice of Rouen. Paris. Wife of Pierre Faverel. The two were arraigned in court by the Faculty of Medicine in Paris for practicing illegally. *Chart.*, II, 149–53, 337; Wickersheimer, I, 100.

1319 Perronnele (*l'erbière*). Paris. She was called from Paris to Conflana "pour la santé" of Mme Mahaut, Comtesse d'Artois, 1319. She evidently engaged in medical practice. Wickersheimer, II, 597.

1322 Agnès Avesot. Paris. Chambermaid of Jeanne Clarisse, and accused with her of practicing illegally. *Chart.*, II, 256; Wickersheimer, I, 10.

Belota. Paris. She was a Jewess, who was accused of practicing illegally. *Chart.*, II, 267; Wickersheimer, I, 66.

Jeanne Clarisse. Paris. She was charged with illegal practice. *Chart.*, II, 256; Wickersheimer, II, 505.

Laurence. Paris. Wife of Jehan de Gaillon. Charged with illegal practice. *Chart.*, II, 256.

1322–24 Jeanne (*conversa*). Paris. Wife of Jean Liblous, with whom she was accused of practicing illegally. *Chart.*, II, 256–57; Wickersheimer, II, 505.

1324–25 Ameline. Paris. She is mentioned with others who practiced illegally. *Chart.*, II, 256.

1326 Sarah of Saint-Gilles. Marseilles. Jewish woman, wife of Abraham. She engaged to clothe and feed Salves de Burgonova and teach him the art of medicine and physic in seven months, on condition that he would turn over to her all the money he earned during that time. Wickersheimer, II, 732.

1348–95 Guillemette Alban. Saint-Flour. *Ibid.*, I, 267.

1350 Jeanne La Douce. Paris. She was condemned by Parliament at the request of the Faculty of Medicine. She "specialized" in cases of ulcer. Félix Aubert, *Le Parlement de Paris, de Philippe le Bel à Charles VII* . . . (Paris, 1890), p. 88; Wickersheimer, II, 507.

1360 Antoinette de Bellegarde. She was accused once of illegal practice and fined 25s., and again of using the knife and fined 10s. Wickersheimer, I, 39.

1404 Marie de Blansy. Paris. With Ives Gilemme, a priest, Perrin Hemery, a locksmith, and Guillaume Floret, a clerk, she invoked devils in an attempt to heal Charles VI. The priest boasted, too, that with the three devils whom he could command, he could free twelve men chained in iron. When the experiment failed, he explained that the men wore the sign of the Cross. The four were publicly condemned and burned. Jean Juvénal des Ursins, "Histoire de Charles VI," in *Mémoires relatifs a l'histoire de France*, ed. M. Michaud (Paris, 1854), p. 425; Wickersheimer, I, 313.

1434 Henriette de Craus. Chamars (Besançon). She was burned for witchcraft and heresy, after being accused of healing by means of incantation and invocation of devils. Wickersheimer, I, 291.

1438 Jeanne de Cusey. Dijon. Wife of the barber, Girart. She was involved in several poisonings and was said to have practiced surgery and medicine, from which she was prohibited under threat of banishment. *Ibid.*, II, 505–6.

1443–48 Jeannette Camus. Dijon. She was imprisoned in Dijon for illegal practice, and when interrogated by physicians and found unable to answer the questions, she was expelled from the town. *Ibid.*, II, 506.

1467 Denise de Partenay (*vieille femme*). Paris. She was arrested by the
      Faculty of Medicine of the University of Paris. Wickersheimer,
      I, 117; *Commentaire de la Faculté de Médecine de l'Université de
      Paris (1395–1516)*, ed. Ernest Wickersheimer; *Collection de
      documents inédits sur l'histoire de France* (Paris, 1915), pp. 238,
      252, 267, 269.

1483 Wife of De Solliès. Toulon. She was accused with her husband of
      caring for the sick in the almshouse. Wickersheimer, I, 133.

1487 Jeanne Villain. Fontvannes (Aube). Wife of Henri Villain. She
      was arrested at Troyes for using witchcraft and incantations in
      healing wounds. *Ibid.*, II, 506.

15c. Margot (*guérisseuse*). She worked at the Hôpital de Lectoure.
      Ibid., II, 537.

England

ca. 1400 Joan. London. She petitioned the King for permission to prac-
      tice medicine, since her husband had been killed in an expedition
      to Wales. Eileen Power, "Some Women Practitioners of Medi-
      cine in the Middle Ages," *Proceedings of the Royal Society of
      Medicine*, Section of the History of Medicine, XV, Part 3
      (1921–22), 20–23.

MIDWIVES

France

1292 Emeline (*ventrière*). Paris, Rue des Escoufles. Her name appears
      in the tax roll of 1292. Géraud, p. 114.
      Jehanne (*sage*). Paris, Rue Symon-le-Franc. *Ibid.*, p. 78.
      Michièle (*ventrière*). Paris, Rue Saint-Martin. Her name appears
      in the tax roll of 1292. *Ibid.*, p. 62.

1408 Pérette (*sage-femme*). Rouen. Wife of Thomas of Rouen. She was
      accused in Paris of magic and sorcery, but was freed of the
      charge. A. Delacous, *Biographie des sages-femmes célèbres . . .*
      (Paris, 1834), pp. 130–36.

15c. Dame de Gaucourt. Charged by Charles VII to visit Jeanne d'Arc
      to confirm her virginity. Her confirmation subdued the rumors
      that Jeanne d'Arc had formed a contract with a demon. *Ibid.*,
      p. 81.
      Dame de Vienne. She accompanied Dame de Gaucourt on her
      visit to Jeanne d'Arc. *Ibid.*, p. 81.
      Thomine Bouteville. She received large sums for her services as
      midwife. Abraham Jacob Rongy, *Childbirth: Yesterday and
      Today* (New York, 1937), pp. 80–81.

Yolande d'Aragon. Mother-in-law of Charles VII of France (1422–61), assisted at more than one lying-in. She was charged by Charles VII to visit Jeanne d'Arc to confirm her virginity. *Ibid.*, p. 80.

Italy

11c. Trotula. Salerno. She became the most famous of the Salernitan women because the *De passionibus mulierum* was ascribed to her. See *Collectio Salernitana* (Naples, 1852), I, 149–61. See Chap. VI, *supra*.

? Abella. Salerno. She is said to have written *De atrabile* and *De natura seminis hominis*. *Ibid.*, I, 372; III, 342.

? Mercuriade. Salerno. She is said to have written the *De crisibus*, *De febre pestilenti*, *De curatione*, and *De unguentis*. *Ibid.*

? Rebecca Guarna. Salerno. She is said to have written the *De febribus*, *De urinis*, and *De embrione*. *Ibid.*, I, 373; III, 342.

1430 Louise Trentacapilli. Salerno. She is said to have practiced medicine. *Ibid.*, I, 373; III, 342.

Germany

1302 Midwife (*hebamme*). Frankfort. Kriegk, I, 13.

NURSES

France

The following nurses were listed in the Paris tax roll of 1292:

Aalès. *Nourrice* of Guillaume, *le perrier*. Géraud, p. 33.

Alison. *Nourrice* of Guillaume. Rue Andri-Malet. *Ibid.*, p. 121.

Avès. *Nourrice* of Andri l'Englais. Rue Neuve. *Ibid.*, p. 76.

Erembourc. *Nourrice* of Oudart de Villers. Rue de Violette. *Ibid.*, p. 120.

Héloyson. *Nourrice* of Guillaume Boucel. Rue des Arsis. *Ibid.*, p. 93.

Jehanne. *Nourrice* of Gefrai Le Lorrain. Parish of Saint-Jehan-en-Grève. *Ibid.*, p. 118.

Jourdenete. *Nourrice* of Guillaume Boucel. Rue des Arsis. *Ibid.*, p. 93.

Mabile. *Nourrice* of Sedile de Falaise. Parish of Saint-Germain. *Ibid.*, p. 16.

Perronele. *Nourrice* of Pierre de Fournay. Rue des Arsis. *Ibid.*, p. 93.

Ysabiau. *Nourrice* of Jehan de Fossez, *ferron*. La Ferronnerie. *Ibid.*, p. 22.

1462 Catherine (*Nourrice*). She was the recipient of public alms. Pierre Rambaud, *L'Assistance publique à Poitiers jusqu'à l'an V* (1912), I, 126.

Jehanne (*nourrice*). She was the recipient of public alms. *Ibid.*

Appendix II

GLOSSARY OF HERBS

HIS GLOSSARY of herbs includes all those mentioned in the text. They are listed under the name by which they are referred to in the text. The glossary gives (1) their popular name; (2) their Latin name (whenever this has been recorded); and (3) their modern name. In the case of the herbs that were said to be used by women, the medical virtues ascribed to them are also given. The chief sources of information on the subject of medieval herbs, which were used for this glossary, were Dioscorides' *De materia medica;* the *Herbarium Apuleii;* Pliny's *Naturalis historiae;* Bartholomew's *De proprietatibus rerum; Sinonoma Bartholomei; Alphita;* Earle's *English Plant Names;* J. Britten and R. Holland's *Dictionary of English Plant Names;* M. Grieve and C. F. Leyel's *Modern Herbal;* and Hermann Fischer's *Mittelalterliche Pflanzenkunde.*

The following abbreviations are used to indicate the source in the text in which the herb is mentioned:

Ab	Abingdon Abbey list
Ar	Arderne
E	*Eneas*
F	*Fierabras*
G	Gaddesden
H	Henslow
Hild.	Hildegarde
M	Popular medical treatises
Men	*Ménagier de Paris*
P	Pertelote's garden
P₁	Wolfram von Eschenbach's *Parzival*
R	Medicinal bath in John Russell's *Boke of Nurture*
R₁	Rutebeuf
W	Wolfram von Eschenbach's *Willehalm*

Absinthium, southernwode, warmot, wermod, wormod. *Artemisia absinthium.* Absinth. (H; Ar)

Acedularum, acetosa, sourdocke. *Rumex acetosa.* Sorrel. (H; Men)

Ache, apio, smallage. *Apium graveolens.* Parsley, wild celery. (H; R; Ar)

Alleluya, alla. *Oxalis acetosella.* Woodsorrel. (H)

Anys, anesum. *Pimpinella anisum.* Anise. (H)

Apio. *See* Ache.

Armoise. See Artemesia.

Artemesia (*armoise*), modorwort, mogwort, muggewede, ragweed. *Artemesia vulgaris.* Mugwort, St. John's plant. (H; M; R₁; Ar) Dioscorides stated that the person who carried artemesia would not become weary, and that he who carried it on his feet would be free from devils and venemous beasts. Made into an ointment with oil of roses, it was helpful to those whose blood hardened about the joints.

Astrologiae, aristologia. *Aristolochia longa, aristolochia rotunda,* and *aristolochia clematitis.* Aristologia. (H) Dioscorides said that round aristologia was so called because it was thought to help women in child-bed. The long aristologia, he stated, was poisonous. The clematitis was effective for curing wounds. The vapor of it would cure fever. Made into an ointment with swine's grease it would cure the "rigors." It was also good for gout.

Avense, auens, herbe Benette. *Geum urbanum.* Avens. (R)

Beteyne, betoyne. *Betonica officinalis.* Betony. (H; M)

Bilgres. Buglos. (R)

Bishop's weed, bishopswort. *See* Bysschopis gres.

Borage. *Borago officinalis.* Borage. (H; Men)

Brasyle, brasel. *Caesalpinia sapan.* (H)

Brere, red. *Rosa.* Rose. (H; Ab)

Bresewort, briswortis, brose wort. *Bellis perenis.* Bruisewort, daisy. (R)

Broklemke. *Veronica beccabunga.* Brooklime. (R)

Brombugle. *See* Bugle.

Bugull, brombugle, bugle, buglosa, gratia dei. *Ajuga reptans.* Bugle, gratia dei, brombugle. (H)

Bysschopis gres. *Veratrum album.* White hellebore. (Ab)

Camamilla, camamille, camemyl. *Anthemis nobilis.* Camomile. (H; R)

Caprifolium. *Lonicera caprifolium.* Woodbine. (H)

Carduus. *Carduus.* Thistle. (H)

Carpus. *See* Fenugrek.

Cassia fistula. *Cassia fistula.* Purging cassia. (Ab)

Centorie, centory. *Erythraea centaurium.* Centaury. (R; P) Pertelote recommended it as a laxative. Dioscorides stated that it was good for ruptures, convulsions, pleurisy, and coughs. He added that it could be taken with wine by those without fever, and with water by those suffering from fever. It was called a panacea because it assuaged all inflammations. It should be gathered at sunrise in a clear season.

Cheke-mete, chikenmete, chyckynwede. *Stellaria media.* Chickweed. (H)

Ciminum, cummin. *Cuminum.* Garden cumin. (Ab)

Cinoglossa. *Cynoglossum officinale.* Hound's tongue. (H)

Clary, oculus Christi, sage. *Salvia verbenaca.* Vervain, sage, clary. (Men)

Coliandrum, coliandre, coriander. *Coriandrum sativum.* Coriander. (Men)

Comfery, confery. *Symphytum officinale.* Comfrey, knitbone, boneset. (H)

Coriander. *See* Coliandrum.

Coule, red; cole. *Brassica oleracea.* Cabbage. (H)

Cowslyppe, corsloppus of Jerusalem. *Primula veris.* Cowslip. (H)

Crousope. *Saponaria officinalis.* Soapwort. (H)

Croysay. *Galium cruciata.* Crosswort. (H)

Cummin. *See* Ciminum.

Dayses, daysey3e. *Consolida minor.* Daisy. (H)

Dendrolibanum. *Rosmarinus officinalis.* Rosemary. (M; H)

Ditayne, dictanmus, diptamnum. *Origanum dictamnus.* Dittany. (M; E; P₁; Men) Dittany was used in *Eneas, Parzival,* and *Willehalm* to stanch blood. Dioscorides stated that it cured wounds from iron or bites from poisonous beasts, that it was a birth hastener, and that its juice and wine were especially helpful to those bitten by serpents. Mixed with the juice of rue it would cure the falling evil. Bartholomew stated that it had the power to drive out arrows and iron from the body. The *Herbarium Apuleii* recommended that for new wounds one should take dittany, stitchwort, and water agrimony, pound them with butter, and lay the ointment on the wound.

Dragans, dragant, dragantea (*trachonte*). *Artemesia dracunculus.* Dragonwort, herb serpentine. (E; Men; P₁)

Ellebor, blac elebre, lungwurt. *Eleborum album, Veratrum album.* White hellebore. *Eleborum nigrum, Veratrum niger.* Christmas rose. (P) Pertelote recommended it to Chauntecleer. Dioscorides stated that white hellebore was effective as a purgative and was good for one who was choking. Black hellebore, he said, was good for phlegm and choler, either alone or with scammony and salt. It was also good for the epileptical, the melancholical, the frantic, the arthritical, and the paralytical. It would cure leprosy. Mixed with acetum in a mouthwash, it was good for the toothache. People sprinkled it about the house, he stated, to ward off evil spirits. When a person dug it, he stood praying to Apollo and Aesculapius, and he observed the eagle's flight, for the bird caused death if he saw one digging the herb.

Endyve, endivia. *Cichorium intybus.* Chicory. (H)

Eufrasia, euphrasie. *Eufrasia officinalis.* Eyebright. (H)

Fenugrek, carpuṣ. *Trigonella foenum-grecum*. Fenugreek. (H)

Flea-bane. *Inula dysenterica*. Middle fleabane. (Ab)

Fumetere. *Fumaria officinalis*. Fumitory. (P) Pertelote recommended it to Chauntecleer. Dioscorides stated that it was good for expelling an overabundance of choler. The juice of it would quicken the sight and draw tears.

Fynel, feniculus. *Foeniculum officinale*. Fennel. (R; Men)

Galanga. *Alpinia officinarum*. Galangal. (Ab)

Gaytre. *Cornus sanguinea*. Cornel. (P) Pertelote included its berries among the medicines Chauntecleer was to take. Dioscorides said that it was good for dysentery and for fluxes and for ulcers of the eyes. It was effective as a dentifrice. If it were burnt, it would drive away serpents.

Gratia dei. *See* Bugull.

Groundyvy, grund-yvy. *Glechoma hederacea*. Ground ivy. (H)

Gynger. *Zinziber officinale*. Ginger. (Ab)

Herbe Benette. *See* Avense.

Herbe Ion, herbe John, herba Ioanhes. *Hypericum perforatum*. St. John's wort. (H; R)

Herbe Roberd, herba Robertus. *Geranium Robertianum*. Herb Robert. (H)

Herbe Water, herba Walteri. *Asperula odorata*. Woodruff, Herb Walter. (H)

Herbe yue, aretica. *Ajuga chamaepitys*. Ground pine, yellow bugle. (P) Pertelote recommended it to Chauntecleer. Dioscorides stated that it was good for the hepatical and nephritical. It was effective in cases of aconite poisoning. It comforted the stomach, when beaten with figs and given like a pill. It was good as a laxative when mixed with honey.

Hertestong, hertis-tong. *Scolopendrium vulgare*. Hart's tongue. (H)

Herwort. *Sonchus oleraceus*. Sow thistle, hare's lettuce, hare's thistle. (H)

Heyhove. *Nepeta glechoma*. Ground ivy. (R)

Heyriff. Clivers. (R)

Holyhokke. *Althea officinalis*. March mallow. (R)

Houseleek. *Sempervivum tectorum*. Houseleek. (Men)

Hyssop. *See* Ysope. (Men)

Katapucia. *Euphorbia lathyris*. Spurge. (P) Pertelote advised Chauntecleer to take it. Dioscorides stated that a pill of it would expel phlegm, choler, and water. The juice would have the same effect, and the leaves mixed with other herbs would do the same.

Laureola, lauriol. *Daphne laureola.* Spurge laurel. (P) Pertelote advised Chauntecleer to take it.

Licoris. *Glycyrrhiza glabra.* Licorice. (Ab; Hild; Men) Hildegarde stated that it was good for the eyes, the voice, and the digestion. Dioscorides had said that it was good for the arteries, but that it must be allowed to melt under the tongue. It would relieve burning in the stomach and would cure liver and kidney troubles. In an ointment, it was good for wounds.

Lily. *Lilium candidum.* White lily. (Hild) Hildegarde recommended it for leprosy. Dioscorides had stated that beaten well with honey, it would relax the nerves, cleanse "leprosies," and clear the face of wrinkles.

Malvas, malvae, yardehok. *Malva sylvestris.* Mallow. (R)

Mandragora, mandrake. *Atropa mandragora.* Mandragora, Satan's apple. (F; Hild) Floripas used it to heal Fierabras's wounds. Hildegarde thought it contained evil spirits. Of all the herbs associated with cures, it was the most enhanced with fanciful legends. Perhaps because the roots were similar to the shape of men, drawings of the plant made the herb appear like a human being, even to the inclusion of mouth and eyes under the thick, spreading leaves that resembled a bushy head of hair. Dioscorides recommended mandragora chiefly as a soporific and anodyne, and stated that the roots seethed in wine, the apples, and the juice were all soporiferous. If the roots were beaten well with acetum, they would heal erysipelas. The juice mixed with honey would expel phlegm and black choler, but would "drive out" life, if taken in too large doses. The herb was helpful in eye medicines, anodynes, and pessums. The new leaves would dissolve all hardnesses, apostumes, and tumors. The *Herbarium Apuleii* prescribed that the roots be dug according to ritual. The juice, it stated, would cure a headache, if smeared on the forehead. Three pennyweights of the herb ground to dust and drunk in wine on seven succeeding days would cure the gout. The herb was endowed with supernatural powers to overcome evil forces. It would drive out "devil sickness." Bartholomew repeated the statements of Dioscorides and added that the "rinds" mixed with wine would heal all kinds of sores, and that because the herb was cold, its fruit would cure the holy fire, choler, and flux of the womb. It would reduce swellings of the body, heal venomous bites.

Margeroum. *Origanum majorana.* Marjoram. (Men)

Marigold, goldes. *Calendula officinalis.* Marigold. (H)

Mather, mayde. *Anthemis cotula.* Stinking mayweed, maytheweed. (H)

Medwort. *Spiraea ulmaria.* Meadowsweet, queen of the meadows. (H)

Melycoyte. (H)

Menta, myntes, myntys. *Mentha viridis.* Spearmint, ortolana. (Men)

Mercurialis. *Mercurialis annua.* Annual mercury. (H)

Modor-wort. *See* Artemesia.

Morsus diaboli. *Scabiosa succisa.* Devil's bit scabious. (H)

Motfelon. *Centaurea nigra.* Knapweed, hardhead. (H)

Mousher, mous-here. *Hieracium pilosella.* Mouse-ear hawkweed. (H)

Mugwort. *See* Artemesia.

Mullein. *Verbascum thapsus.* Mullein. (H)

Netel, red; nettylle. *Urtica.* Nettle. (H; Ar)

Orage. *Chenopodium olidum.* Orache or arrach. (Men)

Osmunde, bon-wurt. *Osmunda regalis.* Royal fern. (H)

Paritory, paritaria, pelyter, piretum. *Parietaria officinalis.* Pellitory. (R)

Parsley, persoly, petrisilinum. *Petrosilinum sativum.* Parsley. (H)

Penidium. (Ab)

Peony, pionia. *Pionia officinalis.* Peony. (Ab)

Periwinkle. *See* Pervynke.

Pervynke. *Vinca minor.* Periwinkle. (H; M)

Pigle, pygle. *Stellaria holostea.* Stitchwort. (H)

Pileole, puliole, tyme. *Thymus serpyllum.* Wild thyme. (H)

Pilosella. *See* Mousher.

Plantayne. *Plantago major.* Plantain. (H; M) Old wives used it for jaundice. Dioscorides stated that the leaves were helpful for all cases of malignant and leprous ulcers. They also stanched blood. They were good for dog bites and inflammations. The juice helped fistulas if poured into them, and if mixed in collyria would relieve pain in the ears, trouble with the eyes, and stop bleeding of the gums. It was good for dysentery, consumption, and flux of the womb.

Primerol. *Primula vulgaris.* Primrose. (H)

Pulegium, riol. *Mentha pulegium.* Pennyroyal. (H)

Ragweed. *See* Artemesia.

Rewe. *Ruta graveolens.* Rue. (Men)

Ribgras, rybbewort. *Plantago lanceolata.* Ribwort. (H)

Riol. *See* Pulegium. (H)

Rose. *See* Brere.

Rosemary. *See* Dendrolibanum.

Sage, salvia. *Salvia officinalis.* Sage. (H; Men)

Sanica, sanicla, sanigle. *Sanicula Europaea.* Sanicle, self-heal. (H)

Sausekele. *See* Solsequium.

Saxifraga. *Pimpinella saxifraga.* Burnet saxifrage. (Ab)

Scabiosa. *Centaurea scabiosa.* Hardhead. (H; R)

Scamonia. *Convolvulus scammonia.* Scammony. (Ab)

Senecion. *Senecio vulgaris.* Groundsell. (H)

Smallache. *See* Ache.

Solsequium, sausekele, solsicle. *Chicorium intybus.* Chicory. (H)

Sorel, sorrelle. *See* Acedula.

Spigurnel. (H)

Tamarindus. *Tamarindus indica.* Tamarind. (Ab)

Tanasetum, tansey. *Tanacetum vulgare.* Tansy. (Men)

Toscane. (R$_1$)

Trachonte. See Dragans.

Treyfoil, trifolium, trifoylee. *Trifolium pratense.* Red clover. (H)

Turbith. *Convolvulus soldanella.* Turpeth. (Ab)

Tyme. *See* Pileole.

Verveyne. Verbena officinalis. Vervain. (H)

Violet. *Viola odorata.* Violet. (H)

Walle wort, walwort. *Sambucus ebulus.* Danewort. (R; Ar)

Wermod, wormod. *See* Absinthium.

Wildflax. *Linaria vulgaris.* Butter and eggs, yellow toad flax, flaxweed. (R)

Wodebynde. *See* Caprifolium.

Wormode. *See* Absinthium.

Yardehok. *See* Malvas.

Ysope, hyssop. *Hyssopus officinalis.* Hyssop. (H)

BIBLIOGRAPHY

APF   Anciens poètes de France
BLVS   Bibliothek des literarische Vereins Stuttgart
EETS   Early English Text Society
SATF   Société des anciens textes français

Abelard. Petri Abaelardi opera. Edited by Victor Cousin. 2 vols., Paris, 1849.

Accounts of the Obedientars of Abingdon Abbey. Edited by R. E. G. Kirk. Camden Society, Vol. LI. London, 1892.

Acta sanctorum Bollandiana. 65 vols., Paris and Rome, 1863 ff.

Aiken, Pauline. "The Summoner's Malady," *Studies in Philology*, XXXIII (1936), 40–44.
    "Vincent de Beauvais and Dame Pertelote's Knowledge of Medicine," *Speculum*, X (1935), 281–87.

Ailred of Rievaulx. Sermones de oneribus in "Patrologiae cursus completus." Edited by J. P. Migne. Series latina, Vol. CXCV, cols. 363–500. Paris, 1855.

Allbutt, Sir T. Clifford. Historical Relations of Medicine and Surgery to the End of the Sixteenth Century. London, 1905.
    Science and Medieval Thought. London, 1901.

Alphita: a Medico-Botanical Glossary from the Bodleian Manuscript, Selden B. 35. Edited by J. L. G. Mowat. Anecdota Oxoniensia, Medieval and Modern Series, Part II. Oxford, 1887.

Amadas et Ydoine. Edited by C. Hippeau. Paris, 1868.

Amherst, the Hon. Alicia M. Tyssen, "A Fifteenth-Century Treatise on Gardening by Mayster Ion Gardener," *Archaeologia*, LIV (2d series, No. 4, 1894), 157–72.

Amis and Amiloun. Edited by MacEdward Leach. EETS, Vol. CCIII. London, 1937.

Amis et Amiles und Jourdains de Blaivies. Edited by Konrad Hofmann. Erlangen, 1882.

Ancren Riwle, The. Edited by James Morton. London, 1853. Camden Society, Vol. LVII.

Archives de l'Hôtel-Dieu de Paris (1157–1300). Edited by Léon Brièle. Paris, 1894. Collection de documents inédits sur l'histoire de France, Vol. XI.

Arderne, John. Treatises of Fistula in Ano. Edited by Sir D'Arcy Power. London, 1910. EETS, Vol. CXXXIX.

Arnaldus de Villanova. Opera. Lyons, 1509.

Atre périlleux, L'. Edited by Brian Woledge. Paris, 1936.

Aubert, Félix. Le Parlement de Paris, de Philippe-le-Bel à Charles VII (1314–1422), son organisation. 2 vols., Paris, 1886–90.

Aucassin and Nicolette. Translated by Eugene Mason. London, 1910.

Aucassin et Nicolette. Edited by Mario Roques. 2d ed., Paris, 1936.

Auctarium chartularii universitatis parisiensis. Edited by Henricus Denifle, Aemilius Chatelain, C. Samaran, and others. 4 vols., Paris, 1894–1938.

Aungier, George James. The History and Antiquities of Syon Monastery. London, 1840.

Aymeri de Narbonne. Edited by Louis Demaison. 2 vols., Paris, 1887. SATF, Vol. XXIV.

Bacon, Roger. "Opus tertium," Opera quaedam hactenus inedita. Edited by J. S. Brewer. London, 1859. Vol. XV.

Bartholomaeus Anglicus. Liber de proprietatibus rerum. All the Propry-tees of Thynges. Translated as by John Trevisa. London, 1495 (?) Liber de proprietatib' rerū Bartholomei anglici. Strasbourg, 1491.

Battandier, Albert. "Sainte Hildegarde, sa vie et ses oeuvres," Revue des questions historiques, XXIII (1883), 395–424.

Bayon, H. P. "Trotula and the Ladies of Salerno: Contribution to the Knowledge of the Transition between Ancient and Medieval Physick," Proceedings of the Royal Society of Medicine, XXXIII[2] (June, 1940), 471–75.

Benedicti regula monachorum. Edited by Edward Woelfflin. Leipzig, 1895.

Benoît de Sainte-More. Le Roman de Troie. Edited by Léopold Con-stans. 6 vols., Paris, 1904–12. SATF, Vols. LII, LVI, LVII, LXII, LXVI, LXVII.

Bernard of Provence. "Commentarium magistri Bernardi provincialis super tabulas Salerni," Collectio Salernitana. Edited by Salvatore De Renzi. Naples, 1852–59. III, 269–328.

Beves of Hampton. Edited by Eugen Kölbing. London, 1894. EETS, Vols. XLVI, XLVIII, LXXV.

Bibliothèque historique du Lyonnais: mémoires, notes et documents pour servir à l'histoire de cette ancienne province et des provinces cir-convoisines de Forez, Beaujolais, Bresse, Dombes et Bugey. Edited by M.-C. and Georges Guige. Lyons, 1886–88.

Black, William George. Folk-Medicine: a Chapter in the History of Cul-ture. London, 1883. Published for the Folk-Lore Society, Vol. XII.

Boccaccio, Giovanni. "Decamerone," *Opera volgari di Giovanni Boccaccio*. Edited by I. Montier. Florence, 1827. Vols. I–V.

Boileau, Étienne. Les Métiers et corporations de . . . Paris, XIIIe siècle: Le libre des métiers d'Étienne Boileau. Edited by René de Lespinasse and François Bonnardot. Paris, 1879.

Boutarel, Maurice. "Les Blessures dans les chansons de geste," *Paris Médical*, No. 17 (April, 1923), pp. 364–66.
   "Le Mauvais Mire, le Charlatan dans les textes du XIIIe siècle," *Paris Médical*, No. 2 (January, 1923), pp. 39–43.

Brehaut, Ernest. An Encyclopedist of the Dark Ages: Isidore of Seville. New York, 1912.

Britten, James, and Robert Holland. A Dictionary of English Plant Names. London, 1866. English Dialect Society, Vols. XXII, XXVI, XLV.

Buckler, Georgina. Anna Comnena, a Study. London, 1929.

Burdett, Henry C. Hospitals and Asylums of the World. 4 vols., London, 1893.

Canisius, Heinrich. Lectiones antiquae, in "Thesaurus monumentorum ecclesiasticorum et historicorum." 4 vols., Amsterdam, 1725.

Capparoni, Pietro. Magistri Salernitani nondum cogniti. London, 1923. Wellcome Historical Medical Museum, Research Studies in Medical History, No. 2.

Cartulaire de Saint-Spire de Corbeil. Edited by E. Coüard-Luys. Rambouillet, 1882.

Cartulaire de l'Université de Montpellier (1191–1400). 2 vols., Montpellier, 1890–1912.

Catalogue of the Archives of M. de Joursanvault. France, 1855–56.

Caxton, William. Dialogues in French and English. Edited by Henry Bradley. London, 1900. EETS, Vol. LXXIX.

Cecil, the Hon. Mrs. Evelyn. A History of Gardening in England. New York, 1910.

Charlemagne. "De Villis," Capitularia regum francorum. Edited by Alfred Boretius. Hanover, 1883. Monumenta Germaniae historica, Legum sectio II, Tomus I.

Charrier, Charlotte. Héloise dans l'histoire et dans la légende. Paris, 1933.

Chaucer, Geoffrey. The Complete Works of Geoffrey Chaucer. Edited by F. N. Robinson. Cambridge, Mass., 1933.

Choix de pièces inédite relatives au règne de Charles VII. Edited by L. Douët-d'Arcq.

Cholmeley, H. P. John of Gaddesden and the Rosa Medicinae. Oxford, 1912.

Chrétien de Troyes. Kristian von Troyes sämtliche Werke. Edited by Wendelin Foerster:
Vol. I. Cligés. Halle, 1921. Edited by Alfons Hilka.
Vol. II. Der Löwenritter (Yvain). Halle, 1887.
Vol. III. Erec und Enide. Halle, 1909.
Vol. IV. Der Karrenritter (Lancelot). Halle, 1899.
Vol. V. Der Percevalroman (Li Contes del Graal). Edited by Alfons Hilka. Halle, 1932.

Christ, Karl. "Die Bibliothek des Klosters Fulda im 16 Jahrhundert; die Handschriften-Verzeichnisse." Zentralblatt für Bibliothekswesen, Vol. LXIV, 1933.

Christine de Pisan. "L'Epistre au dieu d'amours," in Oeuvres poétiques de Christine de Pisan. Edited by Maurice Roy. 3 vols., Paris, 1891. Vol. XXII².

Chronique de Bertrand Du Guesclin, par Cuvelier, La. Edited by Ernest Charrière. Paris, 1839.

Chronique latine de Guillaume de Nangis. Edited by H. Géraud. 2 vols., Paris, 1843. Société de l'histoire de France.

Clay, Rotha May. The Medieval Hospitals of England. London, 1909.

Collectio Salernitana. Edited by Salvatore de Renzi. 5 vols., Naples, 1852–59.

Collins, Joseph. "Medicine in England in Chaucer's Time," Proceedings of the Charaka Club, IV (1916), 139–49.

Commentaire de la Faculté de Médicine de l'Université de Paris (1395–1516). Edited by Ernest Wickersheimer. Paris, 1915. Collection de documents inédits sur l'histoire de France.

Comnena, Princess Anna. The Alexiad. Translated by Elizabeth A. S. Dawes. London, 1928.

Comptes de l'Hôtel des Rois de France aux XIVe and XVe siècles. Edited by L. Douët-d'Arcq. Paris, 1865. Société de l'histoire de France.

Corner, George W., "The Rise of Medicine at Salerno in the Twelfth Century," Annals of Medical History, III (1931), 1–16.

Coulton, G. G. Medieval Panorama. Cambridge and New York, 1939.

Cranage, D. H. S. The Home of the Monk. Cambridge, 1926.

Crawford, Raymond. "The Blessing of Cramp-Rings: a Chapter in the History of the Treatment of Epilepsy," Studies in the History and Method of Science. Edited by Charles Singer. Oxford, 1917.

Crisp, Sir Frank. Medieval Gardens. 2 vols., London, 1924.

Curry, Walter Clyde. Chaucer and the Medieval Sciences. New York, 1926.

Cursor mundi. Edited by Richard Morris. 3 vols., London, 1874–93. EETS, Vols. LVII, LVXIX, LXII, LXVI, LXVIII, XCIX, CI.

Curtin, Roland G. The Medical Superstitions of Precious Stones, Including Notes on the Therapeutics of Other Stones. Reprinted from *Bulletin of the American Academy of Medicine*, Vol. VIII, No. 6 (December, 1907).

Daumet, Georges. "Une Femme-médicin au XIIIe siècle," *Revue des études historiques*, LXXXIV (1918), 69–71.

Davidsohn, Robert. Geschichte von Florenz. 4 vols., Berlin, 1912.

De Chauliac, Guy. Chirurgia magna. Venice, 1498.
  Grande Chirurgie, La. Edited by E. Nicaise, Paris, 1890.
  Here bigŷney ye inuentorie or ye collectorye in chirurgicale parte of medicene compiled and complete î ye yere of our lord, 1363. England? 14–?

Delacoux, A. Biographie des sages-femmes célèbres, anciennes, modernes et contemporaines, avec 20 portraits. Paris, 1834.

Dictionarius of John de Garlande, The. Edited by Thomas Wright, London, 1857. A Volume of Vocabularies. A Library of National Antiquities, Vol. I.

Dictionnaire de biographie française. Edited by J. Balteau, etc. 4 vols., Paris, 1933–39.

Dictionnaire de l'ancienne langue française et de tous ses dialectes du IXe au XVe siècle. Edited by Frédéric Eugène Godefroy. 10 vols., Paris, 1880–1902.

Dioscorides. The Greek Herbal of Dioscorides. Translated by John Goodyer, 1655. Edited by Robert T. Gunther. Oxford, 1934.
  Pedanii Dioscorides Anazerbei. De materia medica. Edited by Curtius Sprengel. 2 vols., Leipzig, 1829–30. In medicorum Graecorum opera quae exstant. Edited by Carolus Gottlob Kühn. Vols. XXV–XXVI.

Dock, Lavinia, L., and Isabel M. Stewart. A Short History of Nursing. New York, 1920.

Documents parisiens du règne de Philippe VI de Valois. Edited by Jules Viard. 2 vols., Paris, 1899.

Dubois, Pierre. De recuperatione Terre Sancte. Edited by Ch.—V. Langlois, Paris, 1891.

Dugdale, William. Monasticon Anglicorum. Edited by J. Caley, H. Ellis, and the Rev. B. Bandinel. 6 vols. in 8, London, 1817–23.

Durmart li Gallois. Edited by Edmund Stengel. Tübingen, 1873. BLVS, Vol. CXVI.

Dizionario di opere anonime e pseudonime di scrittori italiani. Edited by Gaetano Melzi. 3 vols., Milan, 1859.

Duthilloeul, H. R. Douai et Lille au XIIIe siècle. Douai, 1850.

Earle, John. English Plant Names from the Tenth to the Fifteenth Century. Oxford, 1880.

Eckenstein, Lina. Woman under Monasticism. Cambridge, 1896.

Eger and Grime. Edited by James Ralston Caldwell. Cambridge, 1933. Harvard Studies in Comparative Literature, Vol. IX.

Elie de Saint Gille. Edited by Gaston Raynaud. Paris, 1879. SATF, Vol. XII.

Eneas. Edited by J. J. Salverda de Grave. 2 vols., Paris, 1925–29.

English and Scottish Popular Ballads, The. Edited by Francis James Child. 5 vols., Boston, 1882–98.

English Nativity Plays. Edited by Samuel B. Hemingway. New York, 1909.

Evans, Joan. Magical Jewels of the Middle Ages and the Renaissance Particularly in England. Oxford, 1922.

Fierabras. Edited by A. Kroeber and G. Servais. Paris, 1860. APF, Vol. IV.

Firumbras and Otuel and Roland. Edited by Mary Isabelle O'Sullivan. London, 1935. EETS, Vol. CXCVIII.

Fischer, Hermann. Mittelalterliche Pflanzenkunde. Munich, 1929.

Floris and Blancheflour. Edited by A. B. Taylor. Oxford, 1927.

Fontanges, Haryett. Les Femmes Docteurs en médecine dans tous les pays. Paris, 1901.

Gaddesden, John of. Rosa Anglica practica medicinae de capite ad pedes. Edited by Nicolo Scillacio. Pavia, 1492.
    Rosa Anglica sev Rosa medicinae Johannis Anglici. Edited by Winifred Wulff. London, 1923, 1929. Irish Texts Society, Vol. XXV.

Galen, Claudius. Claudii Galen opera omnia. Edited by D. Carolus Gottlob Kühn. 20 vols., Leipzig, 1821–23. Medicorum graecorum opera quae extant. Vols. I–XX.

Garett, Robert Max. "A Middle English Rimed Medical Treatise," Anglia, XXXIV (1911), 163–93.

Garrison, Fielding H. Introduction to the History of Medicine. 3d ed., Philadelphia, 1922.

Gaufrey. Edited by F. Guessard and P. Chabaille. Paris, 1859. APF, Vol. III.

Gaydon. Edited by F. Guessard and S. Luce. Paris, 1862. APF, Vol. VII.

Gerarde, John. The Herball; or, General Historie of Plantes. London, 1597.

Géraud, Hercule. Paris sous Philippe le Bel d'après des documents originaux contenant le rôle de la taille. Paris, 1837.

Gerbert de Montreuil. Le Roman de la Violette. Edited by Douglas L. Buffum. Paris, 1928. SATF, Vol. LXXXI.

Godefred and Theodoric. Vita Sanctae Hildegardis. Edited by J. P. Migne. Patrologiae. . . Series latina. Vol. CXCVII, cols. 91–130.

Godefroy de Paris. Chronique métrique suivie de la taille de Paris en 1313. Edited by J. A. Buchon. Paris, 1827.

Goodman of Paris, The. Edited and translated by Eileen Power. London, 1928.

Gothein, Marie Luise. A History of Garden Art. Edited by Walter P. Wright and translated by Mrs. Archer-Hind. 2 vols., London, 1928.

Gottfried von Strassburg. Tristan. Edited by Friedrich Ranke. Berlin, 1930. In Deutsche Classiker des Mittelalters. Edited by Franz Pfeiffer. Vol. VII.

Gower, John. "Confessio Amantis," *The English Works of John Gower.* Edited by G. C. Macaulay. 2 vols., London, 1900–1901. EETS, Vols. LXXXI–LXXXII.

Grendon, Felix. The Anglo-Saxon Charms. New York, 1909. Reprinted from the *Journal of American Folk-Lore*, XXII, No. 84 (April-June, 1909), 105–237.

Grieve, Mrs. M., and Mrs. C. F. Leyel. A Modern Herbal. 2 vols., New York, 1931.

Grundmann, Herbert, "Die Frauen und die Literatur im Mittelalter," *Archiv für Kulturgeschichte,* XXVI (1936), 129–61.

Gummere, Francis. The Popular Ballad. Boston, 1907.

Gunther, R. T. Early Science in Oxford. 13 vols., Oxford, 1923–30.

Hamilton, George L. "Trotula," *Modern Philology*, IV (October, 1906), 377–80.

Hartmann von Aue. Der Arme Heinrich. Edited by John G. Robertson. London, 1895.
    Iwein. Edited by G. F. Benecke and K. Lachmann. Berlin, 1827.

Hecker, Justus F. C. The Epidemics of the Middle Ages. Translated by B. Guy Babington. London, 1844.

Henry of Lancaster. Le Livre de seyntz medicines. Edited by E. J. Arnould. Oxford, 1940. Anglo-Norman Text Society, Vol. II.

Henryson, Robert. "The Testament of Cresseid," in *The Poems of Robert Henryson*. Edited by W. M. Metcalfe. Paisley, 1917.

Henslow, George. Medical Works of the Fourteenth Century. London, 1899.

"Herbarium of Apuleius, The," in *Leechdoms, Wortcunning, and Star-craft of Early England.* Edited by the Rev. Oswald Cockayne. London, 1864–66. Rolls Series, Vol. XXXV[1].

Hiersemann, Conrad. Die Abschnitte aus der Practica des Trottus in der Salernitanischen Sammelhandscrift "De aegritudinum curatione." Leipzig, 1921.

Hildegarde. Hildegardis causae et curae. Edited by Paulus Kaiser. Leipzig, 1903.
> "Liber vitae meritorum," Analecta Sanctae Hildegardis opera. . . Analecta sacra spicilegio solesmensi parata. Edited by Cardinal Joannes Baptista Pitra. Monte Cassino, 1882. Vol. VIII.
> "Physica," *Hildegardis Abbatissae opera omnia.* Edited by J. P. Migne. Patrologiae. . . Series latina. Paris, 1855. Vol. CXCVII, cols. 1129–1352.

Hippocrates. The Genuine Works of Hippocrates. Translated from the Greek by Francis Adams. 2 vols. in 1, New York, 1891.
> Hippocrates. Translated by W. H. S. Jones. 4 vols., London, 1931.

Histoire littéraire de la France. 37 vols., Paris, 1733–1938.

Historia diplomatica Friderici Secundi: sive, Constitutiones, privilegia, mandata, instrumenta quae supersunt istius imperataris et filiorum ejus. Edited by J. L. A. Huillard-Bréholles. Paris, 1852–61.

Höfler, Max. Volksmedizinische Botanik der Germanen, Vienna, 1908. Quellen und Forshungen zur Deutschen Volkskunde, Vol. V.

Holthausen, F. "Medicinische Gedichte aus einer Stockholmer Hand-schrift," *Anglia,* XVIII (1896), 292–331.

Horn Childe. Edited by Joseph Hall in King Horn. Oxford, 1901. Appendix, pp. 179 ff.

Horn et Rimenhild. Edited by J. R. Lumby. London, 1866. EETS, Vol. XIV.

Hunter, J. English Monastic Libraries. London, 1831.

Hurd-Mead, Kate Campbell. A History of Women in Medicine. Haddam, Conn., 1938.
> "Seven Important Periods in the Evolution of Women in Medicine," *Bulletin of the Women's Medical College of Pennsylvania,* LXXXI, No. 3 (January, 1931), 6–15.

Isidore of Seville. Isidori Hispalensis Episcopi. Etymologiarum sive originum libri xx. Edited by W. M. Lindsay. 2 vols., Oxford, 1911.

James, Montagu R. Ancient Libraries of Canterbury and Dover. Cambridge, 1903.

Jex-Blake, Sophia. Medical Women. Edinburgh, 1872.

Johannes de Mirfeld of St. Bartholomew's, Smithfield; His Life and Works. Edited by Sir Percival Horton-Smith Hartley and Harold Richard Aldridge. Cambridge, 1936.

Jones, Ida B. "Popular Medical Knowledge in Fourteenth-Century English Literature." *Bulletin of the Institute of the History of Medicine.* Part I: V, No. 5 (May, 1937), 405–51. Part 2: V, No. 6 (June, 1937), 538–88.

Juvénal des Ursins, Jean. Histoire de Charles VI. Mémoires rélatifs à l'histoire de France. Edited by M. Michaud. Paris, 1854.

Kantorowicz, Ernst. Kaiser Friedrich der Zweite. Berlin, 1931.

König Dietrich von Bern. Edited by Ernst Martin. Halle, 1867.

Kriegk, G. L. Deutsches Bürgerthum im Mittelalter. 2 vols., Frankfort, 1868.

Kühn, O. Medizinisches aus der altfranzozischen Dichtung, 1904. Abhandlungen zur Geschichte der Medizin, Vol. VIII.

"Lacnunga," *Leechdoms, Wortcunning, and Starcraft of Early England.* Edited by Rev. Oswald Cockayne. Rolls Series, Vol. XXXV³, London, 1864.

Laigle, Mathilde. Le Livre des trois vertus de Christine de Pisan et son milieu historique et littéraire. Paris, 1912. Bibliothèque du XVᵉ siècle, Vol. XVI.

Lallemand, Léon. Histoire de la charité. 4 vols., Paris, 1906.

Lambert li Tors and Alexandre de Bernay. Li Romans d'Alixandre. Edited by Heinrich Michelant. Stuttgart, 1846. BLVS, Vol. XIII.

Lanfranc. Chirurgia parva ad Bernardum and Practica chirurgiae maior. Venice, 1498.
   Science of Cirurgie. Edited by Robert V. Fleischhacker. London, 1894. EETS, Vol. CII.

Langlois, Charles Victor. La Connaissance de la nature et du monde au moyen âge. Paris, 1911.

Lawrence, W. W. "The Tale of Melibeus," Essays and Studies in Honor of Carleton Brown. New York, 1940.

Laȝamon. The Brut. Edited by Sir Frederic Madden. London, 1847.

Leechdoms, Wortcunning, and Starcraft of Early England. Edited by the Rev. Oswald Cockayne. 3 vols., Rolls Series, Vols. XXVI¹, ² ³.

Legacy of the Middle Ages, The. Edited by C. G. Crump and E. F. Jacob. Oxford, 1926.

Lipinska, Mélanie. Les Femmes et le progrès des sciences médicales. Paris, 1930.
   Histoire des femmes médecins. Paris, 1900.

Livre d'Artus, Le. Edited by H. Oskar Sommer. The Vulgate Version of the Arthurian Romances. 7 vols., Washington, 1908-13.

Lloyd, John Uri. Origin and History of All the Pharmacopeial Vegetable Drugs, Chemicals and Preparations. Cincinnati, 1921.

Loomis, Roger Sherman. Celtic Myth and Arthurian Romance. New York, 1927.

Lorris, Guillaume de, and Jean de Meung. Le Roman de la Rose. Edited by Ernest Langlois. 5 vols., Paris, 1914-24. SATF, Vols. LXXI[1, 2, 3, 4, 5].

Luce, Siméon. Histoire de Bertrand du Guesclin et de son époque. 2d ed., Paris, 1882.

Ludus Coventriae; or, The Plaie called Corpus Christi, Cotton MS Vespasian D. viii. Edited by K. S. Block. London, 1922. EETS, Vol. CXX.

Lyf of the Nobel and Crysten Prynce, Charles the Grete, The. Edited by Sidney J. H. Herrtage. London, 1881. EETS, Vols. XXXVI-XXXVII.

Macer floridus: de viribus herbarum. Edited by Julius Sillig. Leipzig, 1832.

Mackay, Dorothy Louise. Les Hôpitaux et la charité à Paris au XIIIe siècle. Paris, 1923.

Malory, Sir Thomas. Le Morte Darthur. Edited by H. Oskar Sommer. 3 vols., London, 1899.

Manheimer, Georg. "Etwas über die Aertze im alten Frankreich," Romanische Forschungen, VI (May, 1890), 581-614.

Marie de France. Die Lais der Marie de France. Edited by Karl Warnke. 3d ed., Halle, 1925.

Mason-Hohl, Elizabeth. "Trotula: Eleventh-Century Gynecologist." A paper read before the American Medical Women's Association, New York City, June 10, 1940. Published in Women in Medicine, No. 70 (October, 1940).

Medici, Michele. Compendio Storico della Scuola Anatomia di Bologna. Bologna, 1857.

Mélanges historiques, choix de documents. Collection de documents inédits sur l'histoire de France. Paris, 1877. Vol. II.

Ménagier de Paris, traité de morale et d'économie domestique composé vers 1393 par un bourgeois parisien, Le. 2 vols., Paris, 1846. La Société des bibliophiles français.

Mercier, Charles A. Leper Houses and Mediaeval Hospitals. London, 1915.

Mervelles de Rigomer par Jehan, Les. Edited by Wendelin Foerster and Hermann Breuer. 2 vols., 1908, 1915. Gesellschaft für Romanische Literatur, Vols. XIX, XXXIX.

Meyer, Paul. "Recettes médicales en français," *Bulletin de la société des anciens textes français* (1906), p. 37 f.
"Les Manuscrits français de Cambridge," *Romania*, XXXII (1903), 18–120.
"Manuscrits médicaux en français," *Romania*, XLIV (1915), 161–214.

Meyer-Steinig, Th., and Karl Sudhoff. Geschichte der Medizin in Überblick mit Abbildungen. Jena, 1922.

Moore, Norman. The History of the Study of Medicine in the British Isles. Oxford, 1908.

Mort Aymeri de Narbonne, La. Edited by J. Couraye du Parc. Paris, 1884.

Mundinus de Luzzi. Anatomia corporis humanis. Leipzig, 1493.

Neckam, Alexander. De laudibus divinae sapientiae. Edited by Thomas Wright. London, 1863. Rolls Series, Vol. XXXIV.
De naturis rerum. Edited by Thomas Wright. London, 1863. Rolls Series, Vol. XXXIV.

Nutting, Adelaide M., and Lavinia L. Dock. A History of Nursing. 4 vols., New York, 1907–12.

Obituaires de la province de Sens. Edited by Auguste Longnon. 4 vols., Paris, 1902. Recueil des historiens de la France, Vols. I–IV.

Ordericus Vitalis. Historia ecclesiastica. Edited by J. P. Migne. Patrologia. . . Series latina. Vol. CLXXXVIII, cols. 17–984.

Otinel. Edited by F. Guessard and H. Michelant. Paris, 1859. APF, Vol. I.

Otuel. Edited by Sidney J. H. Herrtage. London, 1882. EETS, Vol. XXXIX.

Owst, Gerald Robert. Preaching in Medieval England. Cambridge, 1926.

Pansier, P. "La Pratique de l'ophthalmologie dans le moyen-âge latin." *Janus*, IX (1904), 1–26.

Parkinson, John. Paradisi in sole paradisus terrestris; or, A Garden of All Sorts of Pleasant Flowers . . . with a kitchen garden of all manner of herbes, rootes, and fruites for meate or sauce used with cuts, and an orchard of all sorts of fruitbearing trees and shrubbes fit for our land together with the right orderinge planting and preserving of them and their uses and vertues. 2d impression, London, 1656.
Theatrum Botanicum: the Theater of Plants; or, An Herball of a Large Extent. London, 1640.

Partonope of Blois. Edited by A. Trampe Bödtker. London, 1912. EETS, Vol. CIX.

Paston Letters, 1422–1509, The. Edited by James Gairdner. 4 vols., London, 1900–1901.

Paton, Lucy Allen. Studies in the Fairy Mythology of Arthurian Romance. Boston, 1903. Radcliffe College Monographs, No. 13.

Patrologiae cursus completus. Series latina. Edited by J. P. Migne. 221 vols., Paris, 1844–64.

Payne, Joseph Frank. English Medicine in the Anglo-Saxon Times. Oxford, 1904.

Pélerin Richard, Le. La Conquête de Jérusalem. Edited by C. Hippeau. Paris, 1868.

Petrarch, Francis. "Epistolarum de rebus senilibus." *Francisci Petrarchae Florentine, philosophi . . . opera quae extant omnia.* 4 vols. in 1, Basle, 1581.

Petrus Hispanus. Thesaurus pauperum. Venice, 1543.

Pettigrew, Thomas Joseph. "Observations upon the Extracts from an Ancient English Medical MS in the Royal Library of Stockholm," *Archaeologia*, XXX (1844), 419–29.
    On Superstitions Connected with the History and Practice of Medicine and Surgery. Philadelphia, 1844.

Philippe de Rémi. Jehan et Blonde. In Oeuvres poétiques de Philippe de Rémi, Sire de Beaumanoir. Paris, 1885. SATF, Vol. XVII.

Pilcher, Lewis. "The Mondino Myth," *The Medical Library and Historical Journal* (December, 1906).

Pinet, Marie-Josephe. Christine de Pisan, 1364–1430, Étude biographique et littérarie. Paris, 1927.

Pliny the Elder. Historia naturalis. Edited by Carol Mayhoff. 5 vols., Leipzig, 1892–1901.

Power, Sir D'Arcy. "A Short History of St. Bartholomew's Hospital," in *Book of the Celebrities of St. Bartholomew's Hospital, 1123-1923.* London, 1923.

Power, Eileen. Medieval English Nunneries. Cambridge, 1922.
    "Some Women Practitioners of Medicine in the Middle Ages," *Proceedings of the Royal Society of Medicine*, Section of the History of Medicine. XV, Part 3 (1921–22), 20–23.

Puschmann, Theodor. A History of Medical Education. Translated by E. H. Hare. London, 1891.

Rabelais, François. La Vie de Gargantua et de Pantagruel. Oeuvres de Rabelais. Edited by Esmangart et Éloi Johanneau. 9 vols., Paris, 1823.

Raoul von Houdenc. Meraugis von Portlesquez. Edited by Mathias Friedwagner. Halle, 1897.

Rashdall, Hastings. The Universities of Europe in the Middle Ages. Edited by F. M. Powicke and A. B. Emden. 3 vols., Oxford, 1936.

Regestrum visitationum archiepiscopi Rothomagensis. Journal des visites pastorales d'Eude Rigaud, Archevèque de Rouen. 1248–69. Edited by Th. Bonnin. Rouen, 1852.

Regimen sanitatis Salernitanum. Edited and translated into English verse by John Ordronaux. Philadelphia, 1870.

Registrum epistolarum fratris Johannis Peckham archiepiscopi cantuariensis. Edited by C. T. Martin. London, 1882–85. Rolls Series, Vol. I.

Registrum Johannes de Pantissara (1282–1304) episcopi Wyntonienses. Edited by D. Deedes. 2 vols., London, 1916–24. Surrey Record Society.

Reinhard, John Revell. The Old French Romance of Amadas et Ydoine: an Historical Study. Durham, N. C., 1927.

Reliquiae Antiquae. Edited by Thomas Wright and James Orchard Halliwell. 2 vols., London, 1845.

Richars li Beaus. Edited by Wendelin Foerster. Vienna, 1874.

Rigg, George B. The Pharmacist's Botany. New York, 1924.

Rodocanachi, E. La Femme italienne à l'Époque de la Rennaissance. Paris, 1907.

Romance of Tristram and Ysolt by Thomas of Britain, The. Translated from the Old French and Old Norse by Roger Sherman Loomis. New York, 1923.

Roman de Thèbes, Le. Edited by Léopold Constans. 2 vols., Paris, 1890. SATF, Vols. XXX¹ and XXX².

Romans de Durmart le Galois, Li. Edited by Edmund Stengel. Tübingen, 1873. Bibliothek des Litterarischen Vereins, Vol. CXVI.

Rongy, Abraham Jacob. Childbirth: Yesterday and Today. New York, 1937.

Rotuli parliamentorum; ut et petitiones, et placita in Parliamento tempore Edwardi R. I – ad finem Henrici VII. 6 vols., London, 1767–77.

Royal Historie of the Excellent Knight Generides, A. Edited by Frederick J. Furnivall. Hertford, 1865. Roxburghe Club, Vol. LXXXV.

Russell, John. "Boke of Nurture," in Early English Manners and Meals. Edited by Frederick J. Furnivall. London, 1868. EETS, Vol. XXXII, pp. 1–123.

Rutebeuf. "Li Diz de l'Erberie," in *Oeuvres complètes de Rutebeuf, trouvère du XIIIᵉ siècle*. Edited by Achille Jubinal. 2 vols., Paris, 1874.

Sacrorum conciliorum nova et amplissima collectio. Edited by G. D. Mansi. 31 vols., Florence and Venice, 1759–98.

Sarton, George. Introduction to the History of Science. 2 vols., Baltimore, Md., 1927–31.

Scriptores rerum Silesiacarum. Edited by G. A. H. Stenzel. 17 vols. in 9, Breslau, 1835–1902.

"Secretum secretorum," in *Tractibus brevis et utilis ad declarandum quedam obscuri dicta Fratris Rogeri*. Edited by Robert Steele with an English translation from the Arabic by A. S. Fulton. Oxford, 1920.

Seppelt, Franz Xaves. "Mittelalterliche deutsche Hedwigslegenden." *Zeitschrift des Vereins für Geschichte Schlesiens*, XLVIII (1914), 1–18.

Shakespeare, William. "The Merry Wives of Windsor," in *The Works of William Shakespeare*. 10 vols., Stratford-on-Avon, 1904–7.

Siege of Jerusalem, The. Edited by Eugen Kölbing and Mabel Day. London, 1932. EETS, Vol. CLXXXVIII.

Singer, Charles. "The Scientific Views and Visions of Hildegard (1098–1180)," in *Studies in the History and Method of Science*. Oxford, 1917, pp. 1–59.

Singer, Charles, and Dorothea Singer. "The Origin of the Medical School of Salerno," in *Essays on the History of Medicine Presented to Karl Sudhoff*. . . . Edited by Charles Singer and Henry E. Sigerist. Oxford, 1924, pp. 121–38.

Sininoma Bartholomei. A Glossary from a Fourteenth-Century MS in the Library of Pembroke College, Oxford. Edited by J. L. G. Mowat. Oxford, 1882. In Anecdota Oxoniensia. Medieval and Modern Series, Parts I and II.

Sir Ysumbras. Edited by Gustav Schleich. Berlin, 1901.

Spitzner, H. R. Die salernitanische Gynäkologie und Geburtshilfe unter dem Namen der Trotula. Leipzig, 1921.

Stephens, George. "Extracts in Prose and Verse from an Old English Medical Manuscript, Preserved in the Royal Library at Stockholm," *Archâeologia*, XXX (1844), 349–418.

Sudhoff, Karl. Essays in the History of Medicine. Edited by Fielding H. Garrison. New York, 1926.

　　"Medizinische Monatsregeln," *Archiv für Geschichte der Medicin*, II (1908–09), 384 ff.

　　"Die Salernitaner Handschrift in Breslau," *Archiv für Geschichte der Medicin*, XII (1920), 101 ff.

"Zum Regimen sanitatis Salernitanum," *Archiv für Geschichte der Medicin*, IX (1916), 221–49; X (1916), 9–101; XII (1920), 149–80.

Syr Tryamoure. Edited by James Orchard Halliwell. London, 1846. Percy Society, Vol. XVI.

Taunton, Ethelred L. The English Black Monks of St. Benedict. 2 vols., London, 1897.

Theodoric of Thüringen, "Vita Sancte Elizabethae," Thesaurus monumentorum ecclesiasticorum et historicorum, sive Henrici Canisii lectiones antiquae. 4 vols., Amsterdam, 1725.

Thomas Aquinas. Summa contra gentiles. Translated by the English Dominican Fathers. 4 vols. in 5, London, 1923–29.

Thomas of Britain. Le Roman de Tristan. Edited by Joseph Bédier. 2 vols., Paris, 1902. SATF, Vols. XLVI¹ and XLVI².

Thomas of Erceldoune. Sir Tristrem. Edited by Eugen Kölbing. 2 vols., Heilbronn, 1878.

Thompson, E. Margaret. The Carthusian Order in England. London, 1930. Society for Promoting Christian Knowledge.

Thompson, James Westfall. The Literacy of the Laity in the Middle Ages. Berkeley, Calif., 1939.
The Medieval Library. Chicago, 1939.

Thorndike, Lynn. History of Magic and Experimental Science. New York, 1923–34. Vols. I–IV.
"Rufinus: a Forgotten Botanist of the Thirteenth Century," *Isis*, XVIII (July, 1932), 63–76.
"Sanitation, Baths, and Street-Cleaning in the Middle Ages and Renaissance," *Speculum*, III (1928), 192–203.
"Vatican Latin Manuscripts in the History of Science and Medicine," *Isis*, XIII (September, 1929), 53–102.

"Treatise of Walter de Biblesworth, The." A Volume of Vocabularies. Edited by Thomas Wright. London, 1857. A Library of National Antiquities, Vol. I.

Tristrams Saga ok Ísondar. Edited and translated into German by Eugen Kölbing. Heilbronn, 1878.

Trotula of Salerno. "A Medieval Handbook of Gynaecology and Midwifery Preceded by a Section on the Treatment of Wounds and Sane Good Counsel to the Physician Himself Finishing with a Discussion on the Treatment of Scabies," *Irish Texts*. Edited by Winifred Wulff. London, 1934. Fasc. V.
De passionibus mulierum curandorum. Translated by Elizabeth Mason-Hohl. Los Angeles, 1940.

Victoria History of the Counties of England, The. A History of Hampshire and the Isle of Wight. Vol. I edited by H. A. Doubleday; Vol. II, by H. A. Doubleday and W. Page; Vols. III–V, by W. Page. 5 vols., Westminster, 1900–12.

Vie de Vaillant Bertrand du Guesclin d'après la chanson de geste du trouvère Cuvelier et la chronique en prose contemporaine, La. Modernized by Mlle E. Dufaux de la Jonchère, with Introduction and notes by M. Louis Moland. Paris, 1885.

Vision of William concerning Piers the Plowman, The. Edited by W. W. Skeat. London, 1867. B text. EETS, Vol. XXXVIII.

Visitations of Religious Houses in the Diocese of Lincoln. Edited by A. Hamilton Thompson. Lincoln, 1929. Alnwick's Visitations (1436–49). Lincoln Record Society and Canterbury and York Society, Vol. II.

Vita Merlini. Edited by John Jay Parry. *University of Illinois Studies in Language and Literature*, X, No. 3 (August, 1925), 243–380.

"Vocabulary of the Name of Plants, A." *A Volume of Vocabularies*. Edited by Thomas Wright. London, 1857. A Library of National Antiquities, Vol. I.

Von Siebold, Edited by Casper Jac. Versuch einer Geschichte der Geburtshülfe. 3 vols., 2d ed., Tübingen, 1901.

Von Wolfskron, Adolf Ritter. Die Bilder der Hedwigslegende. Vienna, 1846.

Walsh, J. J. Medieval Medicine. London, 1920.
   Old Time Makers of Medicine. New York, 1911.
   The Thirteenth Greatest of Centuries. New York, 1907.

Wedel, Theodore Otto. The Medieval Attitude toward Astrology. New Haven, Conn., 1920.

Wegele, Franz Z. "Die heilige Elisabeth von Thüringen," *Historische Zeitschrift*, V (1861), 351–397.

Weinhold, Karl. Die Deutschen Frauen in dem Mittelalter. 2 vols., Vienna, 1882.

Wickersheimer, Ernest. Dictionnaire biographique des médecins en France au moyen âge. 2 vols. in 1, Paris, 1936.

Willemin, N. X. Monuments français inédits pour servir à l'histoire des arts depuis le XIe siècle jusqu'au commencement du XVIIe. 2 vols., Paris, 1839.

Williams, W. Saint Bernard of Clairvaux. Manchester, 1935. Historical Series, No. 69.

Witkowski, G. J. Histoire des accouchements chez tous les peuples. Paris, 1887.

Wolfram von Eschenbach. Parzifal. Translated into modern German by Wilhelm Stapel. Hamburg, 1937.

    Parzifal und Titurel. Edited by Ernst Martin. 2 vols. Halle, 1900. Germanistische Handbibliothek.

    Willehalm. Edited by Karl Lachmann. 3d ed., Berlin, 1872.

Wright, Thomas. The Homes of Other Days. New York, 1871.

Young, Sidney. Annals of the Barber-Surgeons of London. London, 1890.

Ywain and Gawain. Edited by Gustav Schleich. Leipzig and Oppeln, 1887.

INDEX